PRA

Publishers Note

This edition of *Practical Masonry* is prepared from the fifth
edition published in 1904. This edition incorporated two
addition plates of Grecian and Roman mouldings and also the
Glossary of Terms added when the second edition was
published. Also included were supplements dealing with
estimating, measurement and building stones. As many of the
quarries extant in 1904 are no longer operative and the
methods of measurement and rates for estimating attached
have lapsed into history, these supplements have been omitted
from this new edition.

PRACTICAL MASONRY

A GUIDE TO THE ART OF STONE CUTTING

COMPRISING

THE CONSTRUCTION, SETTING-OUT, AND WORKING OF STAIRS,
CIRCULAR WORK, ARCHES, NICHES, DOMES, PENDENTIVES,
VAULTS, TRACERY WINDOWS, ETC.

BY

WILLIAM R. PURCHASE

With an introduction by
John Fidler, BArch. (Hons), RIBA

ATTIC
BOOKS

Copyright © Attic Books 1987
The Folly, Rhosgoch, Painscastle, Builth Wells, Powys LD2 3LY
First published by Crosby Lockwood Staples London 1895

British Library Cataloguing in Publication Data
Purchase, William R.
   Practical masonry: a guide to the art
   of stone cutting.
   1. Masonry   2. Stone
   1. Title
   693.1   TH5401

   ISBN 0–948083–07–7

Reprinted 1997

Cover design by Jack Bowyer

Printed by Antony Rowe Ltd, Chippenham, Wiltshire

Introduction

This is a good time to be reprinting facsimiles of old books on building technology and craftsmanship. The construction industry has never been so devoted to refurbishment and conservation work and its architects and craftsmen thirst greatly for a better understanding of how buildings and materials were put together. Not only that but they now need tuition on craft processes and techniques still in danger of being lost to the scaffold, to the workshops and to the lecture theatres and classrooms of further and higher education. The history of technical literature in conservation is, to say the least mixed and gaps like these stand out prominently. At the same time, in this Post-Modern era, designers find themselves creating a-new in the fashionable Classical and Neo-vernacular traditions that rely so much on stone and on geometry and detail for effect. Technical drawing has been lost or has been subjugated to other demands for cramped time in the curriculum. The use of stone and its practicalities are also alien subjects to the majority.

I am particularly pleased therefore that Purchase's "Practical Masonry" is here reproduced afresh to instruct and inform another generation in the techniques of using stone. This is not a book designed originally for the expert. William Purchase wrote it from his standpoint as an essentially practical man: as a trained mason and later as a building inspector for the borough of Hove – for beginners, as an introduction to workshop practice and site operations. Along with perhaps Warland's "Modern Practical Masonry" this publication had the greatest influence on masonry training in the first third of the twentieth century and it deserves our interest, not just as a primer for apprentice masons, but also for modern architects and surveyors untrained in basic geometrical setting-out and stone craft skills.

Of course the 18th- and 19th-century pattern books will offer up many more examples of moulding profiles and of architectural detail. You will also find more extensive texts on masons' tools and practice. But this reprint of the first edition of "Practical Masonry" first published in 1895, enhanced by the incorporation of plates on the Orders and of a glossary from the fifth edition of 1904, was never intended to supersede other works. In its modest, down-to-earth-style it initiates the reader instead – in the setting out of complex geometry, in the production of jointing configurations, in accommodating fixings and so on – all with a simplicity reinforced through 400 diagrams.

The publishers have taken the liberty of omitting chapters on estimating and on the then currently available stone. This is forgivable. Taking-off as practised at the death of Queen Victoria can only now be of academic interest and the information on stones is more readily available elsewhere. To be of use to the present generation only the text's timeless messages are reproduced and this reinforces the publisher's wider intent. "Practical Masonry" is here lovingly reborn, to complement from another era, its new stable mate "Masonry Conservation and Restoration": a modern guide to preserving the best of that we inherit from the past for the future.

John Fidler Dip Arch. MA arch. MA conservation.
AA Grad Dipl conservation. RIBA.

Superintending Architect
Historic Buildings and Monuments
Commission for England

PREFACE.

Tins work has been compiled, not with the view of superseding any of the works already published dealing with the architectural or geometrical side of the stone-cutter's art, but as a means of introducing the student of Masonry to the practical work of everyday life in the workshop and on the building. It has no pretensions to instruct skilled workmen, but is intended to initiate young beginners in the craft into the rules and principles of good masonry. It is the result of many years' attentive observation and practical experience, acquired by the Author first as an operative stone-mason, and afterwards as a foreman mason, on some of our largest public buildings.

All the cases commonly met with are worked out, and, when the general principles applying to these are understood, their extension to any unusual question which may occur should not be difficult. The student is assumed, however, to have some knowledge of geometrical drawing and projection, which indeed is indispensable. Most of the examples given are from actual work.

In further explanation of his aim in compiling the volume, the Author may be allowed to cite the subjoined extract from an address delivered a couple of years ago by Mr. J. H. Morton, F.R.I.B.A., President of the Northern Architectural Association.* Mr. Morton said that "it must be allowed that "no trade could be properly learned out of the workshop; "although the men would certainly understand better the "instruction given in the workshop, if they had had the benefit "of a theoretical foundation before proceeding to practice. It

---

* Address at opening of winter session of the Association at Newcastle-on-Tyne, reported in the "Builder" of December 9, 1893.

"was useless to expect the technical school to entirely replace "the apprenticeship system; but having laid the foundation "before entering the workshop, the technical education of the "artisan might go on contemporaneously with the workshop "employment. Many workmen, of excellent practical skill, "worked entirely by rule of thumb, and their efforts would "assuredly prove more successful if guided by the enlightenment "and precision of scientific knowledge. Thus technical educa- "tion might be the means of exalting labour, and of enabling "capable workmen to raise themselves to a higher standard by "the acquisition of a more perfect knowledge of the art of "building."

Any suggestion with which the Author may be favoured, with a view to the improvement of the work in future editions, will be duly acknowledged, and carefully considered as opportunity occurs.

W. R. P.

HOVE. *October*, 1895.

TABLE OF CONTENTS.

TOOLS AND APPLIANCES.—PLATES I. to III.

ARCHES AND JOINTS.—PLATES IV. to VIII.

MASONRY DETAILS.—PLATES IX. to XI.

STAIRCASES.—PLATES XII. to XV.

CIRCULAR WORK (RAMP AND TWIST).—
PLATES XVI. to XIX.

ARCHES, CIRCULAR on PLAN.—PLATES XX. to XXIII.

SKEW ARCH AND NICHES.—PLATES XXIV. to XXVI.

CYLINDRICAL VAULTING.—Plates XXVII. to XXIX.

DOMES & PENDENTIVES.—Plates XXX. to XXXIII.

GROINED VAULTING.—Plates XXXIV. to XXXVII.

GROINED VAULTING (*continued*).—Plates XXXVIII. to XLI.

TRACERY WINDOWS.—Plates XLII. to XLVI.

PRACTICAL MASONRY.

PLATES I., II., III.—TOOLS AND APPLIANCES.

Fig. 1.—The square is of various sizes, and generally made of iron plate about one-eighth of an inch thick; the edges are parallel and at right angles to each other.

It is important that the square should be true, as the accuracy of the work depends entirely upon it, and for this reason it should be frequently tested for correctness.

Fig. 2.—The set square is of several sizes, and made of iron, brass, or zinc plate; it contains a right angle and two angles of forty-five degrees, and is used chiefly for mitres, and setting out on bed of work.

Fig. 3.—The bevel, or shift stock, made of iron or brass, and used for sinkings, bevels, &c.

Fig. 4.—A small tee square of unequal sides, and with right angles, used for sinkings, &c.

Fig. 5.—Mallet of beech, or other hard wood, of various sizes, for striking the cutting tools.

Fig. 6.—Hand hammer of steel, about five pounds in weight, used principally with punch for removing waste, and, in very hard grit stones, it is used also with hammer-headed chisels.

Fig. 7.—The punch: the cutting edge of this tool is about a quarter of an inch wide, and chisel-pointed. It is used with the hammer for removing all superfluous waste.

Fig. 8.—The point, with edge similar to punch, is used with mallet, generally for hard grit or lime stones, and for reducing the irregularities left from punch, leaving the stone in narrow ridges and furrows close down to face.

Fig. 9.—Chisels, of various widths, from a quarter of an inch to one and a half inch wide, used for mouldings, fillets, sinkings, &c.

Figs. 10 & 11.—Boasters, from one and a half inch to three inches wide, used for dressing stone down to smooth faces, and cleaning or finishing mouldings, &c.

Fig. 12.—Broad-tool, about four inches wide, used for tooling.

Fig. 13.—Claw-tool. These are of various sizes, the teeth being cut coarse or fine to suit the texture of the stone. For hard lime stones the teeth at point are about an eighth of an inch wide, and for softer stones from a quarter to three-eighths of an inch wide.

The claw-tool is used after the punch or point, dressing down the ridges still closer to finished face.

Figs. 14 & 15.—Small chisels, of various sizes, for carving, letter-cutting, &c.

Note.—Numbers 8 to 15 are mallet-headed tools, and must never be struck with the hammer, the heads being made to receive the blow of the mallet only.

Fig. 16.—Small chisels, called "splitters," of various sizes; the heads are concave, or cup-headed, as in sketch. When used with an iron hammer (Fig. 21), they cut very smooth and sweet.

They are used mostly for marble work, carving, lettering, &c.

Fig. 17.—Pitching tool: this has a bevelled instead of a cutting edge, and is used with the hammer, for pitching or knocking off the irregularities or waste lumps on stone.

Fig. 18.—Jumper, chisel-pointed and slightly round-nosed; it is wider at cutting edge than the diameter of tool, so that it clears itself in cutting circular holes, for which it is used, chiefly in granite.

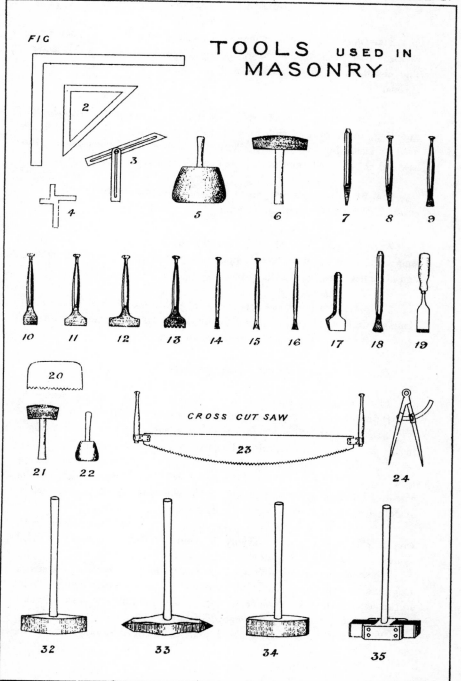

FIG

TOOLS USED IN
MASONRY

Fig. 19.—Chisel for soft stone (this is a general term, and comprises varieties like Bath, Ketton Beer, Caen stone, &c., as well as Alabaster). The chisels have wood handles, and are similar to carpenters' "firmer chisels."

Fig. 20.—Drags for soft stone, of best steel saw-plate, with coarse, middling, and fine teeth, called coarse, seconds, and fine drags. These are used by traversing the face of the stone in all directions, and removing the saw and chisel marks, and finishing to any degree of smoothness required.

Fig. 21.—Iron hammer, about three or four pounds weight, used with cup-headed tools, for carving, lettering, &c.

Fig. 22.—Dummy, of lead or zinc, about three or four pounds in weight, used for striking the soft stone tools; it is handier than the mallet, and at times more convenient to use.

Fig. 23.—Cross-cut saw, of best steel plate, and of various sizes, for cutting soft stone blocks, scantlings, &c.; the teeth are coarse, and broadly set for clearance. Two men are required in using it.

Fig. 24.—Compasses, for setting-out work, &c.

Fig. 25.—Shews sketch of a saw-frame, for hand-sawing, which in practice requires some little skill in framing up to the various sizes.

The frame generally, for good working, should be about two feet longer inside than the length of stone to be sawn, so as to allow for draft.

The heads or ends of frame are made of 4″ × 3″ deal, tapered from near the top to 3½″ × 2″ at the bottom, with a groove or slot for the saw four inches deep by half an inch wide, the angles being rounded off or smoothed to make it easy for the hands.

The stretcher is a piece of pole about three inches in diameter, with iron ferrule at each end, varying in length. Packing pieces are used against the head at each end of stretcher, as shewn.

The couplings are in wrought iron, half an inch in diameter, of various lengths and shapes, as in sketch. These are tightened up with a union screw in the centre, which keeps the saw taut, so that no difficulty is experienced in getting the saw-frame to the required length.

The saw-plate is of iron, about four inches wide by one-tenth of an

PLATE. II

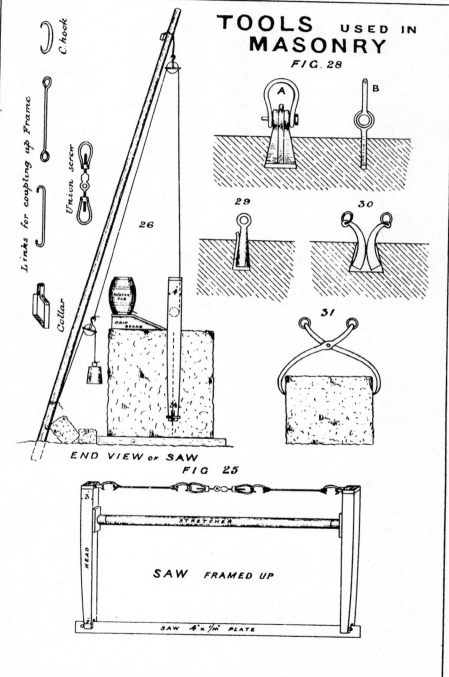

TOOLS USED IN MASONRY
FIG. 28

C. hook

Links for coupling up Frame

Union screw

Collar

26

A

B

29

30

31

WATER TUB

DRIP SOAKS

END VIEW OF SAW
FIG 25

STRETCHER

HEAD

SAW FRAMED UP

SAW 4"x 7/8" PLATE

inch thick, with two holes punched through it, three-quarters of an inch in diameter, at each end, for iron pins, which are inserted to keep the saw in position. The pins are four inches long, and have a small slot the thickness of the saw-plate and one-eighth of an inch deep, fixed with the groove towards the end of the saw; this enables the sawyer to keep the saw straight down the cut, by tapping either end of the pin, should the saw deviate from the vertical line. This slot in the pins is important, as the saw cannot be kept true without this arrangement. The pole, for carrying the saw-frame, is from sixteen to twenty feet long and three or four inches diameter at bottom, and tapering towards the top; a crosspiece and chain is secured nearly at the top of pole to carry the pulley. The pole is kept in position by planting it in the ground, and a rough piece or two of stone is laid against it. The cords for carrying the saw-frame are about half an inch in diameter; small chains are sometimes used, but cords work more easily.

The cord is fastened round the stretcher and over the pulley on top of the pole (which must be vertical to the cut), and then round hook of bottom pulley. The weight must be so adjusted as to allow the saw-frame to be the heavier by about eight or ten pounds; this, however, will depend greatly on the nature of the stone. The position of weight can be raised or lowered to suit the cut by shifting the cord at the bottom of the pole.

The drip-board is of deal, as in sketch, and about two feet long, with sloping side against the cut, and on this is placed the water tub; a small spigot is inserted in the bottom of the tub, and is adjusted to allow the water to trickle down the board, carrying with it the sand, which is also on the board, into the cut. To regulate the supply of water and sand, the sawyer uses a small rake with long handle.

The line of cut for saw should be set out with a plumb rule or bob at each end of the block, and a V shape chase cut in to guide the sawyer in keeping to a true line.

The best sand for cutting is flint road grit, washed through several sieves, all the coarse and fine being rejected, and the medium size only used. A bushel of this sand will cut about twelve feet super of Portland stone.

The saw is drawn backwards and forwards, and the stone cut by the attrition of the saw-plate with the sand and water.

A good sawyer can cut by hand from fifteen to twenty feet super of Portland stone in one day of ten hours.

On large jobs steam stone saw-frames are used, in which, if necessary, from one to twenty cuts may be put in one block at the same time.

Fig. 27.—Shews a method of coping or splitting a block of stone to a required size.

Begin by cutting a V chase on top and two sides of the block, as at *g f e* ; directly under this place a wood skid, and on the top of the skid a long iron bar, which should bone with the line *g f*, or a punch driven in on each side, as at *e*, will do nearly as well. At extreme end place a short skid, as at *h*, and packed up to within an inch of the underside of the block. This is done to prevent the coped piece from breaking under by its own weight, as the fracture would not take the line of direction proposed, but would probably break away from *j* to *k*, and spoil the block.

Sink wedge holes with the punch (at distances apart varying with the nature of the stone) to as fine a point as possible at the bottom of the hole, as in sketch at *b*, so that the wedge will bite or hold when struck with the hammer. The apex of the wedge, which is of iron, is blunt-pointed and about a quarter of an inch wide, so that it does not touch the bottom of the hole, or when struck it would jump out. The holes being cut, the wedges are inserted in each one : care must, however, be taken to keep them upright, so that the cleavage takes the line of direction required. The wedges are now gently tapped with a heavy hammer, till all have got a hold ; then harder blows are given in quick succession, and the fracture takes place.

a shews sketch of wedge, made of iron, and from four to five inches long and one and a half inch wide.

In coping or splitting granite, wedge holes are not cut as in stone, but circular holes are "jumped," one inch or one and a quarter inch in diameter and about five inches deep, at distances apart varying with the obstinacy of the material, and plugs and feathers are inserted and driven in as for stone. The plug is of soft steel, and made tapering as at *c*.

The feathers are thin pieces of iron, concave in section, as shewn at *c* 1. These are first put in the holes, the plugs are then driven in until they become tight, and a few sharp hard blows are all that is necessary to complete the process of splitting. *c* 1 is a plan of *c* to a larger size.

Fig. 28.—Shews a pair of iron lewises used in lifting worked stone for fixing. The lewis consists of a dovetail of three pieces, the two outer pieces being first inserted in the hole, and then the centre piece, which acts as a key, and tightens up the dovetail ; the shackle is next put on, and the bolt is passed through the whole.

Care must be taken to cut the hole to a dovetailed shape, and of the size of the lewis.

A is the front view, and *B* the side view, of the lewises.

Fig. 29.—Shews an iron conical-shaped lewis plug, which is placed in a slightly larger dovetailed hole, a small curved iron plug being inserted by its side, which keys it up. This is used chiefly for worked granite.

Fig. 30.—A pair of chain lewises, consisting of two curved iron plugs with rings for chain; these are inserted in a dovetailed hole, and when tightened up act similarly to the ordinary lewises.

Fig. 31.—A pair of iron dogs, or nippers, with steel-pointed claws, used for lifting rough blocks, and also for fixing.

Fig. 32.—Axe, about twelve or fourteen pounds in weight, chisel-pointed, used on granite for removing the inequalities left by the pick and dressing it similarly to tooled work in stone, shewing the marks or indents in parallel lines.

Fig. 33.—Pick, about sixteen pounds weight, used chiefly on granite, for dressing the inequalities of the rough or rock face down to within half an inch of the finished face; and also used for scabbling blocks of stone roughly to the required shape.

Fig. 34.—Spalling hammer, about twelve to fourteen pounds weight. This has a square edge of about an inch and a quarter, and is a very effectual tool for knocking off rough lumps.

Fig. 35.—Patent axe. The body of this is of iron, with a slot at each end, into which a number of parallel thin plates of steel, chisel-sharpened and of equal length, are inserted and tightly bolted together. This is used for granite, and produces the finest description of face, next to polishing.

Fig. 36.—A pair of trammel heads, or beam compasses, used chiefly for setting out arcs of circles full size; those made of gun-metal, with steel points, are the best, and a set should be large enough to take a rod thirty feet long.

Fig. 37.—A spirit level for fixing.

The following appliances are also required for setting out work :—

A large platform or drawing-board, about ten or twelve feet square; or

PLATE. III.

TOOLS USED IN
MASONRY

Trammel heads & Rod

36

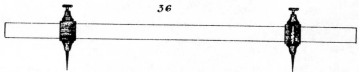

FIG. 37

LEVEL

C 1

Plug
Feather

a　　　*b*　　　*c*

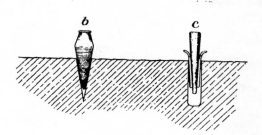

FIG 27

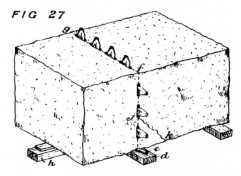

COPING OR SPLITTING BLOCK
BY WEDGES

if larger than this, the better.   It may be fixed either vertically or horizontally.

A standard five-foot rod.

Two or three straight-edges of various lengths.

Deal rods for storey rods, and for setting out lengths of cornices, modillions, dentils, &c.

Pipe-clay and stiff brush, for cleaning off board, rods, &c.

Sheet zinc for moulds, usually No. 9 gauge, this being a good workable thickness.   The lines for face, bed, and section moulds have to be carefully transferred to the sheet zinc, and cut to their proper contour or shapes with shears and files.

The foregoing lists do not comprise all the tools and appliances required for every branch of masonry, but only those which are in common use.

All cutting tools are made of the best cast steel, except the pick, axe, and spalling hammer, which are sometimes of iron, steel pointed and faced.

PLATES IV., V., VI., VII., VIII.—ARCHES AND JOINTS.

THE terms used in connection with the arches here shown may be thus defined :—

The face of the arch is the *front*, or that portion shown in elevation.

The *under-surface* or *soffit* is called the *intrados*, and the outer surface the *extrados*.

The *voussoirs* are the separate arch blocks composing the arch, the central one being the *keystone*.

The *springers* are the first or bottom stones in the arch on either side, and commence with the curve of the arch.

The *skewbacks* generally apply to segmental arches, and are the stones from which an arch springs, and upon which the first arch stones are laid.

The *span* of the arch is the extreme width between the piers or opening ; and the *springing line* is that which connects the two points where the intrados meets the imposts on either side.

The *radius* is the distance between the centre and the curve of the arch.

The highest point in the intrados is called the *crown*, and the height of this point above the springing is termed the *rise* of the arch.

The *centre* is a point or points from which the arch is struck ; and lines drawn from this centre or centres to the arch are radiating joints, and are also called *normals*.

All joints in arches should be radii of the circle, circles, or ellipses forming the curve of the arch, and will therefore converge to the centre or centres from which these are struck.

Fig. 1.—Shews a segmental arch, in which the above-mentioned terms are illustrated.

Fig. 2.—Is a semi-circular arch, *A B* being the span and *C D* the rise ; the left-hand half has the ordinary joints radiating from the centre

C, and the right-hand half, with rebated or step joints, also radiating from the centre C. This last is a sound and effective joint where great strength is required, and there is also no tendency to sliding of the voussoirs.

Fig. 3.—Shews a semi-oval arch, approaching in form that of the ellipse, and struck with three centres. This form of arch has a somewhat crippled appearance at the junction of the small and large curves, and is on that account not pleasing to the eye.

It may be here observed that the true ellipse is obtained from an oblique section of the cone, and no portion of its curve is any part of a circle, and cannot, therefore, be drawn by the compasses or from centres.

The method of setting out and drawing the joints requires but little explanation, $A\ B$ being the span, $C\ E$ the rise, and $D\ D$ and F the centres, from which the curve is struck, the joints converging to their respective centres.

The left-hand half is shown with square bonding on face, and the right-hand half shows line of extrados.

Fig. 4.—Is a semi-elliptic arch.

On comparing this with the arch shewn in Fig. 3, which is of the same span and rise, the gracefulness of the elliptic arch will be apparent.

To draw the arch joints :—

Divide the soffit into any convenient number of parts, and find the foci by taking C as centre and $A\ E$ equal to half the major axis as radius, and describe an arc cutting line $A\ B$, giving the foci F and F. From F and F draw lines to H (one of the divisions for the arch joints) and bisect the angle $F\ H\ F$; the bisecting line $H\ O$ produced will be perpendicular to the tangent of the curve, and will give a true radiating joint.

The other joints are found in the same manner.

Fig. 5.—Shews an equilateral arch, described about an equilateral triangle $A\ B\ C$, the centres A and B being at the extremities of the span.

The joints are drawn to the radii or centres A and B.

Fig. 6.—Is the lancet-shaped arch, described about an acute-angled triangle $A\ B\ C$, the radius $D\ E$ being longer than the span of the arch.

The joints are drawn from the centres D and D.

ARCHES AND JOINTS

FIG . 1

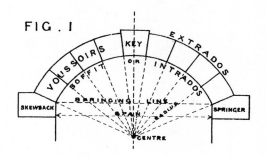

FIG 2

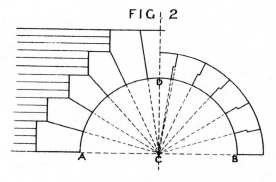

FIG 3

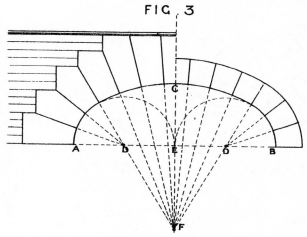

PLATE. V.

ARCHES AND JOINTS

FIG. 4

FIG. 5

FIG. 6

FIG. 7

FIG. 8

Fig. 7.—Is the drop arch, described about an obtuse-angled triangle $A B C$, the radius $D E$ being shorter than the span of the arch.

The joints are drawn from the centres D and D.

Fig. 8.—Shews the four-centred or Tudor arch, $A B$ being the span and $C D$ the rise ; two of its centres, $E E$, are on the springing line, and the two others, $F F$, below it.

The joints are drawn from the centres $E E$ and $F F$ as shewn, and require no further description.

Fig. 9.—Is a Tudor arch, based on the curve of the hyperbola.

Let $A B$ be the span and $C D$ the rise of arch : erect perpendicular at A, and make it equal in height to two-fifths of the rise as at $A C$, and draw the line $C D$. Now divide the lines $A C$ and $C D$ each into six equal parts, and draw lines from 1 to 1, 2 to 2, 3 to 3, &c., and the line drawn through the intersection of these points gives the curve of one side of the arch. The other side is obtained similarly.

A thin flexible lath is generally used for guidance in drawing an easy curve through the points of intersection.

To draw the arch joints :—

At any point in the curve, say at E, drop a perpendicular on to the springing line, as F, make $B G$ equal $B F$, and from G draw line to E, which is a tangent to the curve, and erect the perpendicular $E H$, giving the arch joint required.

The other joints are described in the same manner.

Fig. 10.—Is another example of the Tudor arch, and is a parabolic curve.

Let $A B$ be the span and $C D$ the rise, erect a perpendicular at A and make it equal in height to half the rise, and proceed as in previous figure.

To draw the arch joints :—

At any point in the curve, say at E, draw the chord line $B D$ and bisect it in F; join $F G$ cutting the curve in H, and from the point E draw line $E J$ parallel to $E F$, cutting $F G$ in J; on the line $F G$ make $H K$ equal to $H J$, join $E K$ and draw $E L$ perpendicular to $K E$, thus giving the joint line required.

The other joints are described in a similar manner.

Fig. 11.—Shews a straight or flat arch, the joints radiating to a common centre.

On the right-hand half the joints are not continued through to soffit or top, but have a small portion squared on, thus relieving the acute angles of arch blocks, which are otherwise liable to fracture.

The springer on left hand has additional strength in having a square seating on skewback.

In flat arches a camber of an eighth of an inch in a foot to soffit is usually given to allow for any depression or settlement.

Fig. 12.—Is another example of the flat arch ; the left-hand half has rebated or step joints, and the right-hand half has joggle joints.   All these joints converge to a common centre.

Fig. 13.—In this figure a lintel with double joggle vertical joints is given.

Fig. 14.—Shews a lintel with curved joggle joints, and is an example not often met with.

The form of joint in figs. 12, 13 and 14 is a little wasteful of material ; but where stone is plentiful and in small blocks, good lintels may be obtained.   Many examples of these may be seen in our modern Gothic buildings.

Fig. 15.—Illustrates a window or door head with quadrant corners ; the stretching-piece or key is in one stone, with arch-joints resting on the skewbacks.

Fig. 16.—Is another form of head, the square seating on each stone giving additional strength, and the joints converge to a common centre.

Fig. 17.—Shews three joints used in landings.

A is a joggle joint, commonly called He and She joggle.   A tongue is cut slightly tapering on one edge, fitting into a corresponding groove worked in the other edge.   Run in with cement it forms a strong and secure joint.

B is a rebated joint ; this is sometimes undercut.

C is a bird's mouth joint.   Grooves are roughly cut in on the edges of these joints opposite each other, and the cavities run with cement grout. Slate dowels are also laid longitudinally in the joint and run with cement.

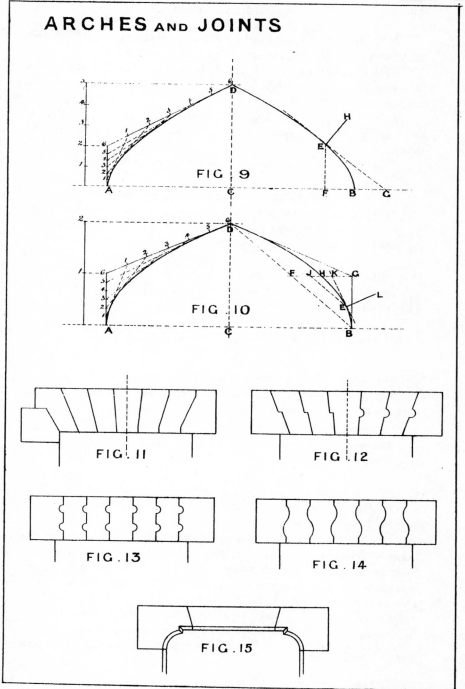

PLATE. VI.

ARCHES AND JOINTS

FIG 9

FIG 10

FIG. 11

FIG. 12

FIG. 13

FIG. 14

FIG. 15

Fig. 18.—A horizontal lintel or architrave spanning an opening, with an apparent vertical joint, but concealing a secret arch joint.

This is used chiefly in colonnades, porticoes, &c., where stones of a sufficient length are not attainable, and sometimes also for convenience of hoisting and fixing.

An indent is formed the shape of the reverse of a wedge in joint of abutment, and a wedge-shape projection is cut in keystone fitting neatly into the indent.

This makes a good and secure joint without dowelling or cramping.

Fig. 19.—Shews sketch of weather or saddle joint in cornice.

This joint is made by leaving at each end of the stone a ridge or roll, the formation of which is generally left till after fixing. This roll effectually prevents the water running through the joint. The roll is not usually seen from the front, as the nose of cornice is continued straight through the joint, although it is also in some cases made a feature of.

This joint is used chiefly for cornices and window sills where there is a large projection.

A cross-section of the joint shows thus :

Fig. 20.—Exhibits a rebated joint in gable coping.

This joint is serviceable, inasmuch as it keeps the water out of the joint and the wall dry, although it is somewhat expensive.

Fig. 21.—An example of various bed joints in stone spires, being respectively—

A. A horizontal bed joint.

B. A bed joint at right angles to batter.

C. A rebated or stepped bed joint.

D. A joggle or tabled joint.

The bed joints of the stones are usually cut at right angles to the batter or face of the spire, as at *B;* but horizontal beds, as at *A*, are supposed not to involve so much thrust at the base. But for obviating any outward tendency, a chain or rod-bond united at the angles, and inserted in a cavity at the base of the spire, is sometimes used.

The two bed joints *C* and *D* are both a little wasteful of material, but for stability and strength these are by far the best form of joints.

A word may be said as to the thickness of the work; this will depend

PLATE. VII.

ARCHES AND JOINTS

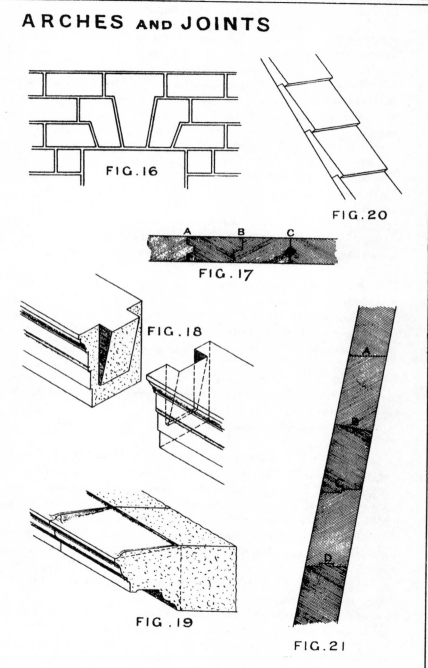

FIG. 16

FIG. 20

FIG. 17

FIG. 18

FIG. 19

FIG. 21

chiefly on the height of the spire and the quality of the stone. From ten or twelve inches at the base, diminishing to six inches or even less at the top, may be generally considered sufficient.

The stone-work of the spire of Salisbury Cathedral (the spire, reckoning from the tower, being 204 feet in height), is two feet thick at the base, and gradually diminishes in thickness to about twenty feet above the tower, where it is reduced to nine inches, and is continued at that thickness to the capstone at the summit.

Fig. 22.—Gives plan of part of one course of stones in the Eddystone lighthouse. The stones are held in position by being dovetailed one into the other.

This form of joint is seldom used, except in works requiring great strength, such as sea-walls, breakwaters, &c. It is also an expensive joint, on account of the large amount of labour, and the waste of material.

Fig. 23.—Shews ashlar in courses with joggle joints.

This is a very unusual form of joint, and is used no doubt more for effect than utility. There is a waste of material and labour, and a better result may be obtained by the use of slate cramps. However, there are several examples of it in modern buildings in London.

Fig. 24.—A seating to sill, with a slate or copper dowel to prevent lateral motion. Mortices are cut opposite to each other in the two beds, and the dowel made secure by being run in with cement.

The dowel is a most useful adjunct in good and secure fixing.

Fig. 25.—*A* is a metal cramp for securing joints together. A chase or groove is cut in the stone of a sufficient width and depth, and at each end a mortice hole is cut to the exact size of inside of cramp, so that it fits tightly, and requires to be tapped into its place ; it is then run with melted brimstone or cement.

The use of iron cramps and dowels in connection with stone is generally attended with some danger, on account of the iron rusting, which causes an increase in size, and subsequent fractures and discolouration of the stone. But if the iron is properly protected by galvanizing or japanning, the risk is reduced to a minimum.

The best metals for cramps, dowels, &c., are copper, gun metal, or brass, but these are expensive and are therefore not much used.

B is an example of a slate cramp also used for connecting joints

ARCHES AND JOINTS

FIG . 22

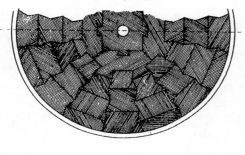

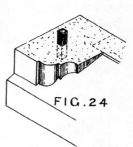

FIG.24

FIG . 23

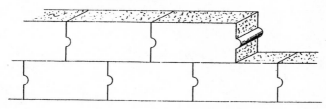

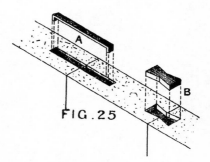

A

B

FIG.25

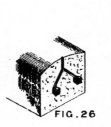

FIG.26

FIG.27

together, and is an excellent and economical substitute for metal. It is made dovetail in shape, let in flush to the bed of the stone, and then run in with cement.

Fig. 26.—Shews a plugged or lead dowelled joint. This is chiefly used in copings, curbs, strings, arches, &c., and prevents the joint working loose or "drawing."

Two holes, dovetail in shape, are sunk in the joints opposite each other and a small groove is cut from the top to each hole and run in with lead.

Slate dowels are sometimes used for this purpose, and run in with cement.

Fig. 27.—Shews a lewis, or holding down bolt, let in a dovetail hole and run in with lead.

Plates IX., X., XI.—MASONRY DETAILS.

Fig. 1.—To form a PLANE SURFACE from a rough block, when the surface is of considerable size.

Four small cubes of beech, or any hard wood, about two inches square, wrought perfectly true, are used for this purpose, and are termed *boning pegs*.

Commence at the end of block by chiselling at each corner a sinking sufficiently low to take out any irregularities which from observation can be seen, and repeat the operation at the opposite end; place the pegs at each corner, and apply straight-edge on them as at *a b* and *c d*, sight through (or "bone," as it is usually termed), and adjust sinkings until the bottom of straight-edges are out of winding and in one plane. This being done, work straight drafts from sinkings *a* to *b*, *c* to *d*, *b* to *c*, and from *d* to *a*, point off superfluous stone and dress to a finished face.

To prove that the face is a true plane, apply the straight-edge on the diagonals *a* to *c* and *b* to *d*; these should be perfectly straight, and the surface also in every part should coincide with the straight-edge.

The use of the "boning pegs" on large surfaces is obvious, as all that is necessary is to sink the small corners where the adjustment is required, instead of reworking a long draft each time.

When the surface to be formed is not too large, a draft may be sunk across at each end of the stone, and boned through with straight-edge, and the above operation repeated without the pegs.

With regard to beds and joints, these are worked to perfectly true and straight surfaces, and the chisel drafts round the margin should form sharp and straight arrises.

The point may be freely used in the centre of bed, but care must be taken not to work the bed hollow, because when the stone is bedded, there would be undue pressure on the outer edges, which would be liable to cause fracture of the stone.

Fig. 2.—To form a WINDING SURFACE.

For this purpose two rules or straight-edges are used, one having parallel edges, the other with divergent edges giving the amount of twist that is required. The distance apart at which the two rules are to be placed is generally defined by two light iron rods connecting them together.

Commence by working drafts across each end of block, and apply the rules as at *c d* and *e f*, and bone the upper edges of rules until they coincide. Work straight drafts on sides at *c e* and *d f*, dividing each end into an equal number of parts as *g h i*, and cut straight drafts through from *g* to *g*, *h* to *h*, and *i* to *i*. The remaining portion is now to be subdivided, and straight drafts worked through from corresponding point to point until the whole surface is finished. The drafts must not be worked parallel to sides, or a correct winding surface will not be formed.

Winding surfaces are used chiefly in skew arches, with spiral beds and joints, and in the beds of coping to curved wing walls, and also to the soffit of winders in stairs, an example of which will be given in the next section.

Fig. 3.—To form a CYLINDRICAL SURFACE.

Square the ends of block off to a plane bed or joint, and scribe in section mould of cylinder ; mark the centre and diagonal lines on as *a b, c d, e f, g h*, at each end, care being taken to keep these lines each in the same plane, as the accuracy of the cylinder depends on their coinciding.

Point off superfluous stone roughly to near the surface, and chisel straight drafts from *a* to *a'*, *b* to *b'*, *c* to *c'*, &c. ; divide the spaces from *a* to *e*, *a* to *g*, &c., into as many parts as are convenient, and work drafts through to corresponding divisions, until the whole surface is finished to a true cylindrical face.

Fig. 4.—To work a LENGTH OF CORNICE out of a rectangular block of stone.

The beds, joints, and nosing being first worked, scribe in section mould on each joint, draw a line at pleasure close to the profile of moulding as at *a b*, forming a wedge-shape piece to be removed, which rough off with the punch right through the block, taking out smaller checks roughly as shewn at *c d e, e f g*.

Fig. 5.—The next process is shewn here, from *A* to *B*. This is to roughly chisel out the shape of mouldings to within about an eighth of an inch of the finished surface. This being done, clean through the mouldings, as shewn at *B* to *C*, by aid of round-nose and narrow chisels, and some-

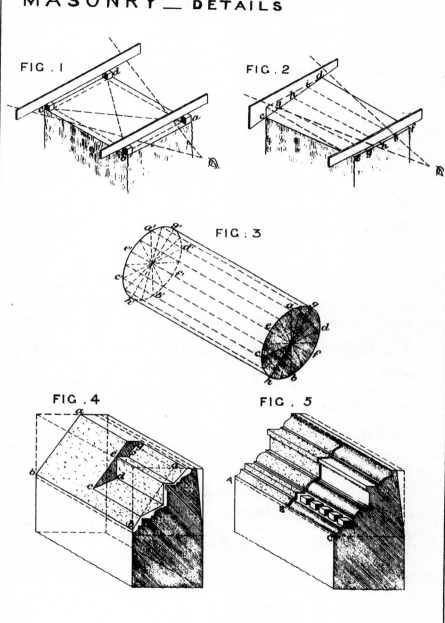

MASONRY _ DETAILS

FIG . 1

FIG . 2

FIG : 3

FIG . 4

FIG . 5

times for extra finish smooth over with the boaster, applying the straight-edge frequently to test the accuracy of working; and lastly, cutting in the dentils.

This method of working applies to all other forms of mouldings.

Fig. 6.—Exhibits the various forms of dressing stone commonly used.

A shews a boasted or chiselled face, sometimes termed droved work. The face is finished with a boaster, and the strokes are generally regular and parallel to each other.

In hard grit stones this face is usually left as finished, and when, as in the case of a building, the whole of the ashlar and plain work is chiselled to the same angle of inclination, the effect is pleasing.

In softer stones a finished face is formed by rubbing the boasted face with sand and water, and removing all chisel marks; it is then called plain ashlar.

B shews ashlar with tooled face.

This is formed with a broad tool, or wide boaster, by a regular succession of strokes, parallel to each other, extending across the whole width of stone, and when finished shews a series of flutes or channels,

thus, the size of flutes depending on the texture of the stone.

Considerable skill is required in tooling neatly, and the tooling is somewhat costly, the surface having first to be worked to a boasted face.

C shews ashlar with pick or pecked face, and tooled margin.

This is produced with a point, or in the case of granite with the pick, and can be worked to any degree of fineness.

D shews ashlar with punched rock face, and tooled margin.

This is similar to the last mentioned, but much coarser. In producing it, the punch is driven in almost vertical to the face until the stone bursts out, leaving a series of cavities. When regularly done it looks well, and is very effective, and for large work it gives the appearance of boldness and solidity.

E shews ashlar with broached face, and tooled margin.

This is produced with a point, which forms a furrow with rough ridges, and is worked across the stone to the required angle.

F shews ashlar with rusticated face, and tooled margin.

This is worked with small chisels and points, and sunk down about half an inch, leaving a plain narrow margin on face; the pattern is irregular, but easily adapted to any space.

G is a rebated or rustic quoin, with vermiculated face.

This is cut out with small chisels, and has the appearance of being worm-eaten.

Fig. 7.—To set out the ENTASIS, or SWELL, of a COLUMN.

Draw the centre line or axis, and set off the height of column, *L K*, and top and bottom diameters, *O P*, *N M*. Divide the column into four equal parts. The first part, to *A*, will be continued straight, and of the same diameter as at bottom. Divide the remaining three-fourths of column, from *A* to *K*, into any number of equal parts (in this example four), as at *B C D K*. At *A*, with radius *F* or *G*, draw the semicircle *F G*. Now project the top diameter *O P*, cutting the semicircle at *4 4*, and divide the arc of semi *F 4*, into four equal parts, as at 1, 2, 3, 4, answering to the number of divisions in column, and draw lines parallel to *F G*, as 1 1, 2 2, 3 3, 4 4; at *b b*, *c c*, *d d*, set off diameters 1 1, 2 2, and 3 3, respectively.

Bend a flexible rod to the points *O*, *d*, *c*, *b*, *F*, and draw the curved line, which repeat on opposite side from *P* to *G*, giving the required entasis.

Fig. 8.—Shews another method of setting out the entasis of columns, by a curve known as the conchoid of Nicomedes. This is preferable to the former method, and the result is more graceful and regular.

The height of column and bottom and top diameter being determined, draw centre line *H G*, and line *B J* at right angles to the same; set off the bottom semi-diameter, *A B*, from *D*, the extreme point of top diameter, cutting the centre line at *E*. Then from *D*, through *E*, produce the line to *F*, cutting base line at *C*, and from this point, *C*, as a centre, draw through the axis of column any number of lines, as *a*, *a*, *a*, &c., on each of which from the centre line towards the circumference set off the distance *A B*, as *a b*.

Through the points D, a, a, a, &c., draw the curve, by aid of a flexible rod, giving the entasis required.

This curve may be also struck with a trammel, which gives a continuous line, and is the most perfect of any system adopted.

The base perpendicular and hypothenuse being obtained by the preceding method, take three wood straight-edges, as $G H$, $B J$, and $D F$; fasten $G H$ and $J B$ together; at H plough a groove in middle of $G H$ from top to bottom, and at the point C on the rule $J B$ fix a pin; then on the rule $D F$ set off the distance $D E$, equal to $A B$, the bottom semi-diameter of column, and at the point E fix a button, whose head must be exactly fitted to the groove made in $G H$, in which it is to slide; and at the other extremity of the rule $D F$ cut a slot right through from F to L, the length being not less than the difference between $C E$ and $C B$, and of sufficient size to allow the slot to pass evenly the pin fixed at C.

The trammel being thus completed, place the rule $G H$ so that the middle of groove is directly over the centre line of column, move the rod $D F$ along the groove $G B$, and with its point D, on which is fixed a pencil, describe the continuous curve from D to A, thus giving the required entasis.

To diminish or enlarge a Section Mould.

Fig. 9.—Shews section of a cornice mould, which it is proposed to diminish to the height of a given line, $c d$, and the projection of the same diminishing in like proportion.

Draw the vertical line $a b$, and produce horizontal line of mouldings on to same; with $a b$ as base, erect an isosceles or equilateral triangle, $a o b$, and on this set off the given height, $c d$; from $a b$ draw the lines of mouldings converging to apex o, cutting the given line $c d$, which is proportionately divided by it.

For the projection: On line $g b$ draw the triangle $g h b$, and project vertical lines from points in the moulding, and draw converging lines to apex, h. The line $e f$ is obtained by finding a fourth proportional, namely, as $a b$ is to $c d$, so is $g b$ to $e f$. This may be solved by geometrical construction or by calculation. Transfer divisions from $c d$ and $e f$, Fig. 9, to $c d$ and $e f$, Fig. 10, produce the lines to intersections, and draw in the mouldings.

The above principle will apply to any description of mouldings, and any number of points in the members may be obtained similarly.

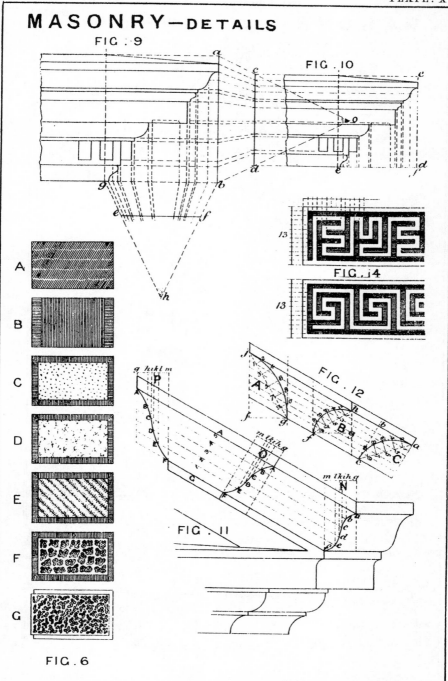

PLATE. X.

MASONRY—DETAILS

FIG : 9

FIG . 10

FIG . 14

FIG . 12

FIG . 11

A

B

C

D

E

F

G

FIG . 6

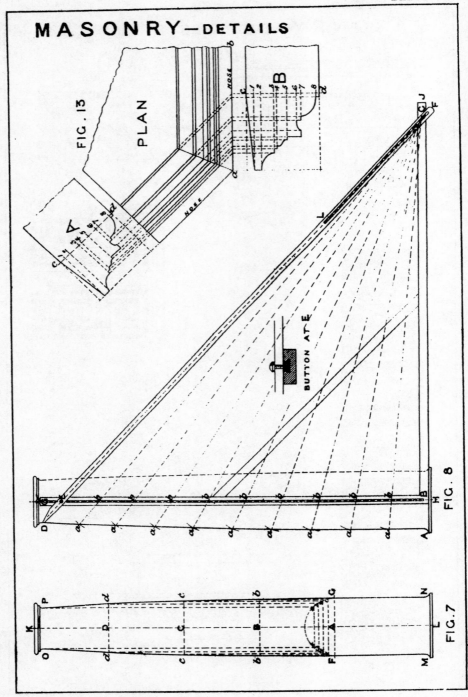

Raking Moulds.

[Raking is a term applied to such members of a building as are inclined from the level or horizontal, and frequently occur, especially in pediments, &c.]

Fig. 11.—To find the RAKING MOULD of the CYMA RECTA, or OGEE, in a pediment.

Let N be the given section of horizontal mould. Divide the distance from A to G into any number of parts, as 1, 2, 3, 4, 5, and draw lines through these points parallel to Aa, cutting N at b, c, d, e, and at a, b, c, d, e, f, erect perpendiculars, as g, h, i, k, l, m. At O draw a line parallel to the nosing, and transfer the distance g, h, i, k, l, m from N, and from these points project lines at right angles to the nosing, cutting raking lines, 1, 2, 3, 4, 5, at A, B, C, D, E, F. Through these points of intersection draw the section of cyma recta raking mould. This section will form a true mitre at N and P.

The section of ogee, as in that of a broken pediment at P, is obtained similarly.

Fig. 12.—To find the RAKING MOULD of a CAVETTO, or HOLLOW.

Let C be the given section. Draw a cord line from a to c, and divide it into any number of equal parts (in this example six), or divide the square line from c to b into the same number, and lines drawn through these divisions parallel to rake will equally divide all chord lines. Draw ordinates at chord lines ac, fh, and gj, and set off 1 2, 3 4, 5 6, &c., and through the points 2, 4, 6, 8, at A and B, draw the curve giving the true sections.

All other sections of mouldings are obtained in a similar manner.

To produce a Stretching Mould, or Elongated Section of Square Mould.

Fig. 13.—Shews plan of octagonal angle, the square section of moulding being given at A.

To find the section to apply on line $a\,b$, project lines of section A on to plan and produce them through to line $a\,b$, and project these lines at right angles to the same. Set off the height and lines 1, 2, 3, 4, 5, &c., on $d\,c$ at A, and transfer to $d\,c$ on B, and produce them through. The intersection of these lines will give points in the section, and for the contour of the mouldings, any number of points may be projected in the same manner, and the mould thus completed.

This section applies also to the mitre of a right angle.

Fig. 14.—Shews two examples of the Grecian fret, or key pattern.

These are produced by dividing the height into any number of equal parts, and the horizontal line into the same divisions; draw the lines through, intersecting each other, forming small squares, and then trace the pattern, the bands and sinkings being of equal width.

PLATES XII., XIII., XIV., XV.—STAIRCASES.

The *tread* of a step is the upper or horizontal surface, and the *riser* is the front vertical face or upright portion of the step. The *soffit* is the under surface, and in spandrel steps is inclined from the horizontal. The *nosing* is the front edge of the tread and riser, and is either square or moulded.

Flyers are straight steps with parallel edges.

Winders are steps with converging edges on tread, and parallel edges on riser, and generally a twisting surface on soffit.

For general purposes, the tread of a step should not be more than twelve inches, nor less than nine inches, and the rise of a step should not be more than seven inches, nor less than five and a half inches.

The proportion usually adopted, is any two numbers between the above sizes which, multiplied together, produce sixty-six : namely, a twelve-inch tread by a five and a half-inch rise equals sixty-six, or $11 \times 6 = 66$, and again $11\frac{1}{2} \times 5\frac{3}{4} = 66$. This, however, may be slightly modified—as, for instance, a ten-inch tread and a six and a half-inch rise equals sixty-five—but the rule may be relied upon as safe in working to.

A staircase easy of ascent, and in other respects desirable, is one in which all the steps are flyers, and having quarter or half-space landings.

Long straight flights with more than twelve steps before reaching a landing should be avoided.

Where there is a deficiency of room or space, winders have to be introduced ; and these, if properly arranged, need not interfere with the ease of the ascent.

In setting out, for the purpose of making the moulds, the first point to be considered (the plan being satisfactory) is the width of the tread and the rise of the steps ; these are best obtained by measuring the length and width of the well-hole, and the height from floor to floor, from the actual work if practicable, and then dividing out the dimensions thus obtained into the number of steps on deal rods, or it may be also found by calculation. The height rod is called the storey rod, and this and the other rods are afterwards used in the fixing of the stairs.

Fig. 1.—To set out a SPANDREL STEP MOULD.

Draw a line $F B$, and line $B C$ at right angles to same, and on $F B$ set off $A B$ the width of tread, and on $B C$ the height of rise. From A to C draw a diagonal line cutting tread and rise at their extremities, and draw parallel to it line $E D$ for soffit, of a sufficient depth proportioned to the strength of the stone, which in this example is put at two inches. For the back rebate, set off from A to F one and a quarter inches, and from F draw line square with soffit to E ; for the front rebate draw line from C to G square with the rise and set off one and a quarter inches, and from G draw line square with soffit to D, thus forming a birdsmouth, the exact reverse of the back rebate.

Allow one-twelfth of an inch for joint, which cut off from the mould as shewn by double line at C G D.

A moulding or astragal nosing is added on to front of riser when necessary.

Fig. 2.—Shews plan of a stair generally considered to be a good type.

It starts with two curtail steps and four flyers reaching a quarter-space landing, then eleven more flyers, reaching a half-space landing, and five flyers to the top landing.

The setting out of this requires no explanation.

Fig. 3.—Shews part plan of stair with winders.

Fig. 4.—Is a development of the plan of stair shown in Fig. 3.

The stairs should be set out to full size, and on a large board or platform, and it may be here noted that the riser lines only are essential to the setting out, both on plan and section, the moulded nosing being seldom shewn.

Begin with the plan and draw the wall lines $C D E$, and lines $F G H$ for the quoin ends, draw centre line $A B$, and on this line from No. 13 to 20 divide out the winders equal to the width of tread of the flyers, dividing the quoin ends into the same number of parts.

These need not be equal in size, and a better result will be obtained if the ends are a little graduated from the flyers to the angle winder each

PLATE. XII.

STAIRS

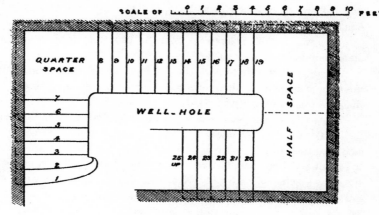

QUARTER SPACE

WELL-HOLE

HALF SPACE

FIG. 2

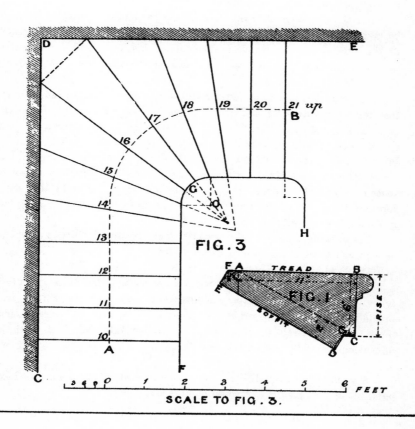

FIG. 3

FIG. 1

SCALE TO FIG. 3.

way, in order to get a good tread and an easy line to the soffit and handrail.

The winders will not radiate from the centre of quadrant *O*, but at a distance outside of it, as shewn.

Another method is to draw the development of quoin end, and adjust the ends of steps upon this, until a good line for soffit is obtained, the riser lines are then transferred to plan.

To set up the development for quoin ends, draw parallel lines on board for the rise as given by storey rod, and begin at bottom by drawing No. 10 step, and then No. 11 and No. 12 steps. No. 13 is the first winder. Set off the exact size from riser to riser on plan and draw on board, proceeding in the same manner with No. 14. Nos. 15, 16, and 17 are segmental on plan. Set off the developed size of each respectively, following on with Nos. 18, 19, &c., till each is drawn, so that the distance from riser of No. 10 to riser of landing No. 21 equals the distance of quoin ends on plan, when unfolded or stretched out in a straight line.

For the development of the wall end, set out similarly to the preceding by taking the distance of each winder on the wall line of plan, and setting up the same on board. No. 16 is taken across the corner and not into the angle; with this exception the wall end is stretched out in a straight line.

The soffit has now to be considered. Begin by drawing an easy curved line, taking up with soffit of flyer No. 11 and finishing with soffit of landing No. 21, keeping the rebates about the same size as the ordinary steps; this it is not always possible to do, but the size of rebate is not of so much importance as that of having a good soffit line. The rebates to winders are in every instance of the same square section as the flyers, but in some cases may be less in depth or greater, according as the soffit line cuts through them. A small reverse should be made from the development for guidance in working each.

For drawing the soffit a flexible lath or rod is used, by means of which an easy and graceful line is obtained.

Fig. 5.—The bed moulds for winders are made of deal laths about two inches wide by half an inch thick, nailed together as shewn in sketch. The mould is scribed on the tread of the stone to be worked, allowance being made for the back rebate, and also for the tailing into wall, both of these dimensions being figured on the mould.

Fig. 6.—Shews a well-hole mould, usually made of sheet zinc, used for guidance in drawing the segmental quoin ends.

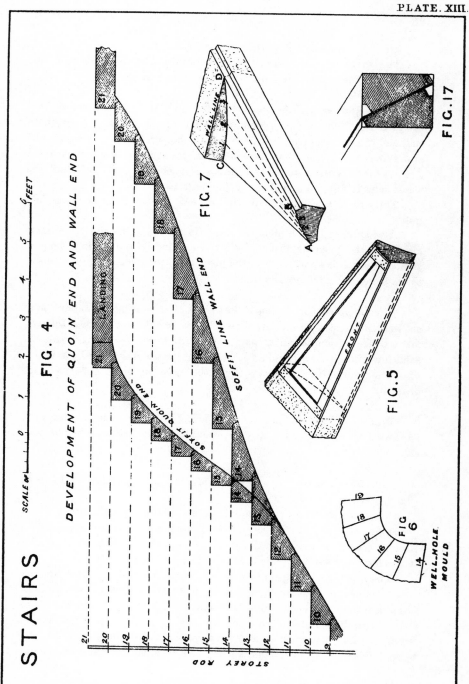

STAIRS

PLATE. XIII.

SCALE

FEET

FIG. 4

DEVELOPMENT OF QUOIN END AND WALL END

STOREY ROD

LANDING

SOFFIT QUOIN END

SOFFIT LINE WALL END

FIG. 7

WALL LINE

FIG. 5

FRONT

FIG. 17

FIG. 6

WELL-HOLE. MOULD

Fig. 7.—Shews sketch of soffit of winder.

The working of the winder is plain straightforward work with the exception of the soffit, which is a twisted or warped surface.

Cut in draft as *A B* on quoin end and sink draft to templet at wall end as *C D*. Point off superfluous waste and divide drafts *A B* on quoin end, and *C D* at wall end, into four equal parts, as 1, 2, 3; work straight drafts from 1 to 1, 2 to 2, and 3 to 3; these are again to be subdivided and straight drafts worked to corresponding divisions at each end, until the whole soffit is finished to a true winding surface.

The square seating at wall end is left on for a good fixing into wall.

A winding stair with moulded nosing is worked in precisely the same manner as the foregoing, the only difference being in the nosing, the projection of which is an addition to the plain riser, the riser lines, rebates and soffits being in every case identical.

A point which should not be lost sight of in setting out stairs, is to see that sufficient head room is allowed; this should not be less than six feet six inches from nose of steps to soffit of flight over,—that is to say, the soffit line of flight over should not cut below an arc described by a radius of six feet six inches, taken from the nose of either of the steps beneath.

Fig. 8.—Shews the plan of a winding staircase in a circular well, supported by a solid newel in the centre, the newel being worked on each step.

Fig. 9.—Is a sectional elevation of the winding staircase shown in Fig. 8.

It may be known to most of our readers, that if a piece of paper of the shape of a right-angled triangle be wound round a cylinder, the hypothenuse (or long side of the triangle) will generate a curve winding round the cylinder in the form of a spiral. This curve is called the helix.

The soffit line of the stairs winding round the well, and line winding round the newel, is the helix, and the soffit contained between these lines forms a true helical plane; the development therefore of each end of the step is a straight line on the soffit, so that no setting up on section is required. The plan must be laid down on the board full size, the treads being divided out equally, and each step being similar and alike, one mould

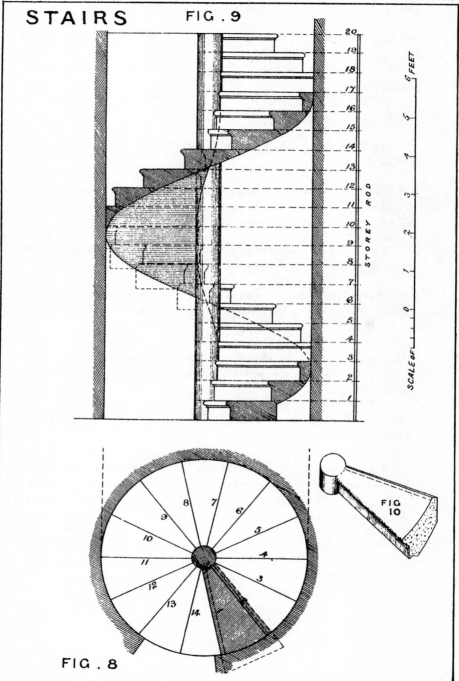

STAIRS

FIG. 9

PLATE. XIV

STOREY ROD

SCALE OF 6 FEET

FIG 10

FIG. 8

will do for the whole. The starting step is not generally worked on the soffit, but is kept solid.

The hatched line on Fig. 8 shews the extreme size of the bed mould of each winder.

The method of working the soffits will be similar to that described in Fig. 7.

Fig. 10.—Shews a sketch of one of the winders, the newel forming a portion of each.

Fig. 11.—Shews part plan of a circular stair, having an open newel or central well ; this stair, like the preceding Figs. 8 and 9, is an example of the helix, the soffit being a helical plane.

Fig. 12.—Is development of part of the circular stair of Fig. 11, shewing quoin and wall end, the lines of soffit to each being straight.

The student who has worked out the previous examples of stairs, will not, it is presumed, require any further instruction on the setting out and working.

Figs. 13 and 14 are elevations of quoin ends, and sections of two forms of bracketed stairs suitable for good buildings, such as hotels, mansions, clubs, &c.

Fig. 15.—Is a section of solid square steps, suitable for warehouses, workshops, &c., where great strength is required.

Fig. 16.—Shews section of a simple form of steps, consisting of treads and risers in separate pieces, worked out of two inch or two and a half-inch stuff.   These are chiefly used for back stairs, area steps, &c., and are inexpensive in construction.

Fig. 17.—Shews method of sawing spandrel steps, one out of the other, so as to economise stone.

The treads of winders are also sawn in a similar manner.

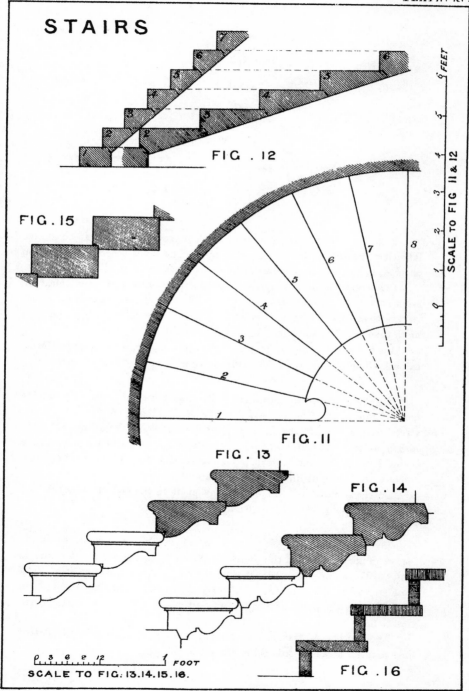

PLATE. XV.

STAIRS

FIG. 12

FIG. 15

FIG. 11

6 FEET

SCALE TO FIG 11 & 12

FIG. 13

FIG. 14

FIG. 16

0   3   6   9   12   1 FOOT
SCALE TO FIG. 13.14.15.16.

Plates XVI., XVII., XVIII., XIX.—CIRCULAR WORK (RAMP and TWIST).

Fig. 1.—Shews plan of part of a TERRACE STAIR, with BALUSTRADE following the inclination or rake of steps. The balustrade being circular on plan, it necessitates a certain amount of twist in its working.

[The method here adopted is not, perhaps, the most economical as regards material; but it is comprehensible, and more true in form when worked than with a complication of moulds and bevels, and the material is more than saved in the labour of working.]

Begin by laying down the plan full size on a large board or platform, carefully dividing the space for balusters equally.

Fig. 2.—Set up the elevation to developed line of convex or outside face of plinth—that is to say, the line $A\ B\ C$ on plan (Fig. 1), when stretched out or unfolded in a straight line, is equal to or of the same length as the horizontal line $A\ B\ C$. The line of inclination will be a helical line, as the steps are of equal tread and rise; therefore the plinth starts with a straight line parallel to the nose of steps.

On elevation set off the joints (convenient to the size of stone) for the plinth and capping at right angles to the line of rake.

Fig. 3.—Set up the elevation to developed line of concave or inside face of plinth, and set off the joints which are to coincide with the outside joints. To obtain these, transfer the joints from the elevation (Fig. 2) of outside face to the plan (Fig. 1), and produce the joint lines through to inside face by the lines radiating from centre, and re-transfer to the inside elevation.

The method of drawing the section of steps is shown by the dotted lines and the notation, this being similar to the plan.

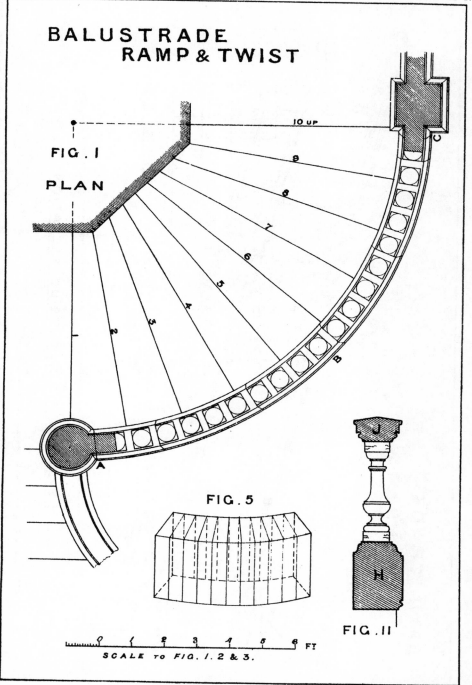

PLATE. XVI.

BALUSTRADE
RAMP & TWIST

FIG. I

PLAN

10 UP

9

8

7

6

5

4

3

2

C

B

A

FIG. 5

FIG. 11

J

H

SCALE TO FIG. 1. 2 & 3.

0   1   2   3   4   5   6 FT

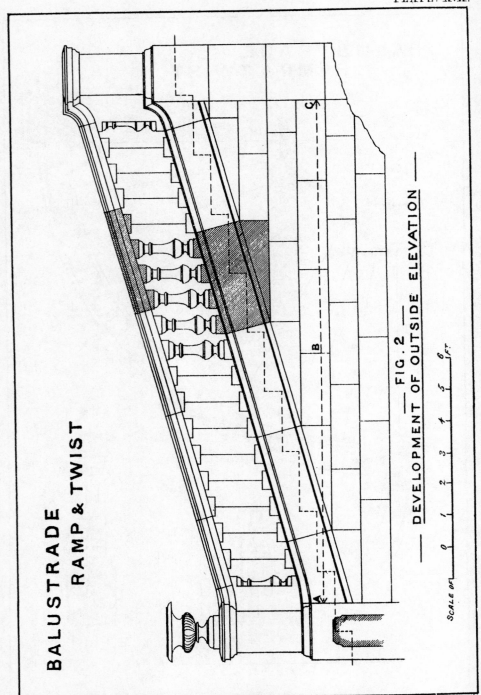

PLATE. XVII.

BALUSTRADE
RAMP & TWIST

FIG. 2

DEVELOPMENT OF OUTSIDE ELEVATION

SCALE OF   0   1   2   3   4   5   6 FT.

For the purpose of illustrating the making of the moulds and the working of the stones a plinth block and length of capping are taken, as shewn by hatched lines on Figs. 2 and 3. The details are given to a larger scale.

To work the Plinth Block.

The block of stone required to work the plinth block will be rectangular in shape, of the extreme length of the bed mould; and the width will be equal to the distance across the chord line, and the height will be that of the face moulds.

Fig. 4.—*A* Shews bed mould of the plinth.

B Shews face mould of convex or outside face.

C Shews face mould of concave or inside face.

Begin by working the bottom bed to a true plane; then work the top bed parallel to it as a surface of operation, and taken to the height of the face mould. Scribe the bed mould in on each bed, care being taken to bone the points through so that the moulds are perfectly out of twist; proceed to work the concave and convex surfaces. For guidance in working this to a true form radiating lines are marked on the beds taken from the mould, and the straight edge is applied on the face to drafts coinciding with these. At this stage the stone is a true segment of a hollow cylinder, as shewn in Fig. 5. Now apply face mould *B* (Fig. 4), to convex face, and face mould *C* (Fig. 4), to concave face, and scribe them in to their respective shapes; work the joints through, and scribe in the section mould *H* (Fig. 11).

The top bed, or surface of operation, is now done with, except at the high corner which forms the bed of the baluster seating. Point off the superfluous waste down to the top of the other baluster seatings, and clean through the beds and sides of these from outside to inside face, as shewn by sketch Fig. 6.

Next gauge the distance taken from the bed or section mould of seating of baluster to the convex and concave faces, and work the same, thus completing the baluster plinths.

For guidance in working the ogee raking mouldings, a bending strip or thin lath, and one or two small reverses cut to section of moulding, will be all that is required, and the stone is finished as in sketch (Fig. 7).

Each of the other plinth stones are worked similarly.

PLATE. XVIII.

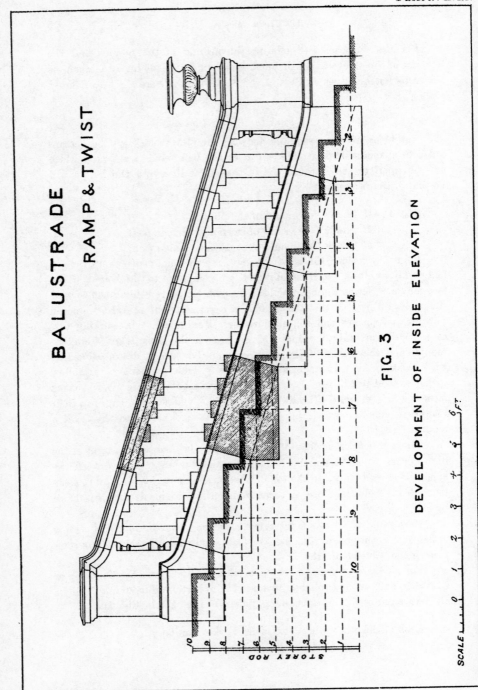

BALUSTRADE
RAMP & TWIST

FIG. 3

DEVELOPMENT OF INSIDE ELEVATION

SCALE 0 1 2 3 4 5 6 FT.

STOREY ROD

PLATE. XIX.

FIG. 4

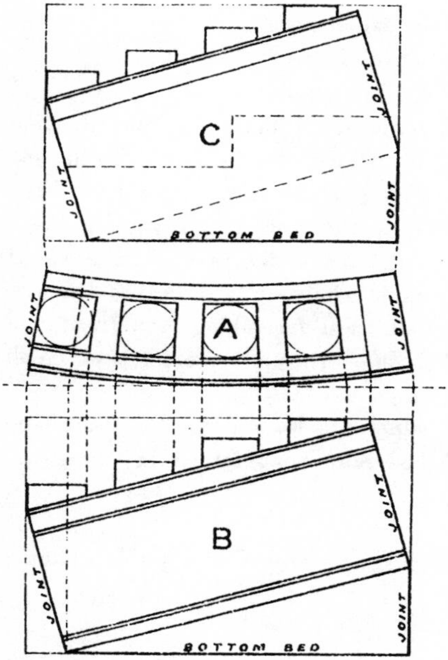

FIG. 8

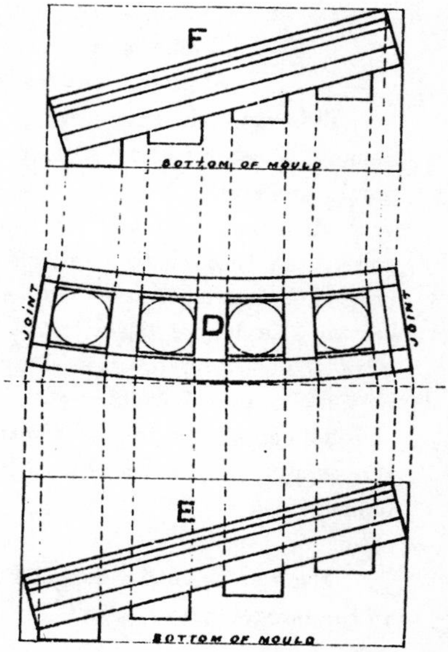

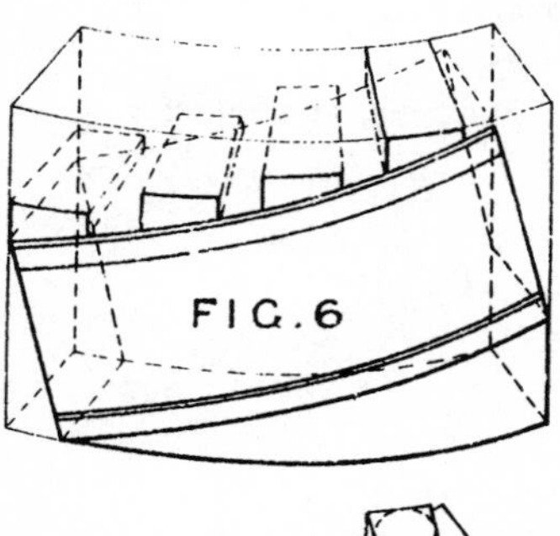

C

BOTTOM BED

A

JOINT

JOINT

B

JOINT

JOINT

BOTTOM BED

F

BOTTOM OF MOULD

JOINT

JOINT

D

E

BOTTOM OF MOULD

FIG. 6

FIG. 9

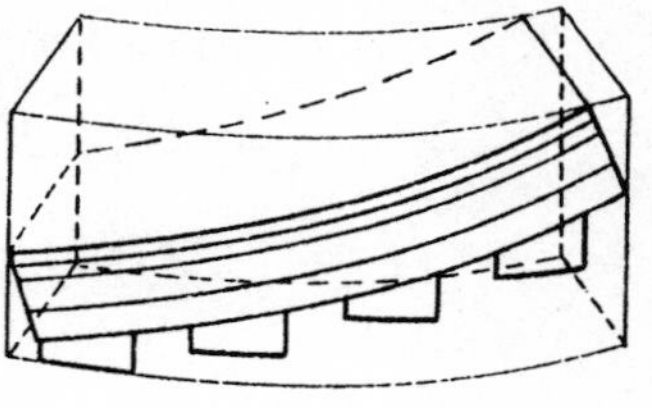

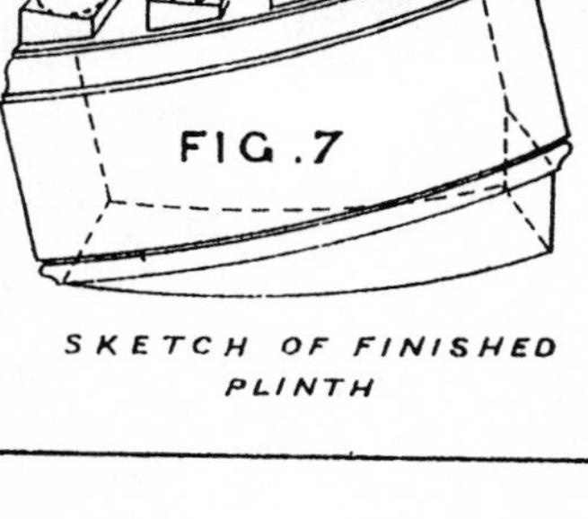

FIG. 7

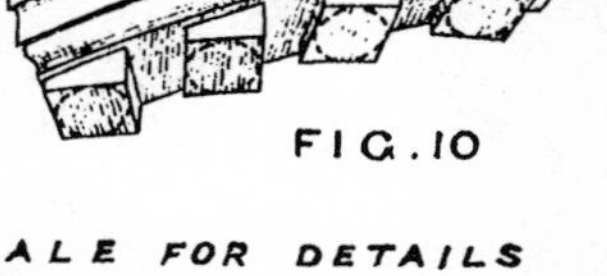

FIG. 10

SKETCH OF FINISHED
PLINTH

SCALE FOR DETAILS

0   1   2   3 FT

To work the Length of Capping.

Fig. 8.—*D* Shews bed mould of the capping.
 E Shews face mould of convex face.
 F Shews face mould of concave face.

This stone is worked in precisely the same manner as the plinth—namely, by working first a segment of a cylinder to the shape of the bed mould and to the height of the face mould, as in sketch (Fig. 5). Then apply face moulds *E* and *F* respectively to the convex and concave faces, and scribe them in. Work off the joints, and scribe in section mould *J* (Fig. 11); next point off the superfluous waste, and work the baluster seatings as before described. Trammel lines for raking mouldings and work them through, assisted by a bending strip and reverses, and finish by working off the saddle-back weathering.

The small seating or plinth of baluster is worked on the plinth and the capping, in order that a level bed may be obtained in fixing the baluster.

Each of the other lengths of capping are worked in a similar manner to the foregoing.

Fig. 10.—Is sketch of length of capping finished; this is slightly tilted up, so as to shew the baluster plinths.

Fig. 11.—Shews section of the plinth, capping, and baluster.

Plates XX., XXI., XXII., XXIII.—ARCHES.

CIRCULAR ON PLAN, OR ARCHES OF DOUBLE CURVATURE.

To describe the construction of a Semi-circular Arch in a Cylindrical Wall, the development of which on convex or outside face is a semi-circle, and on concave or inside face is a semi-ellipse, the soffit radiating to a centre at springing, and the crown of the arch level or at right angles to the vertical face of the wall.

Fig. 1.—Shews plan of the arch, *B C D* being the opening, the arch radiating to *O*, the centre of the cylinder.

To set up the Elevation on the Development for the Face Moulds.

Fig. 2.—Develop the segment *A B C* of convex face (Fig. 1), setting out the length on springing line as *A B C* from *C* as the centre ; erect a perpendicular as centre line, and describe with *C B* as radius half of the semi-circle. Set off the joints radiating to the centre *C* corresponding to the number of arch joints required, which in this example is seven. The square bonding *d a, f b, g c* of vertical and horizontal joints may be of varied sizes. The radiating joints (here shewn) are made equal in length from the soffit, and for this purpose from the centre *C* describe a quadrant, cutting the joints at *a b c*.

To find the Development of Concave Face.

Fig. 3.—Divide the quadrant *B K* (Fig. 2), into any number of equal parts—in this example seven—and draw the ordinates 1, 2, 3, 4, 5, 6, projecting the same on to the springing line, and transfer these to the segment line *B C* on plan (Fig. 1) as 1, 2, 3, 4, 5, 6, and from these points draw radiating lines from the centre *O*, cutting the segment *B' C'* at 1', 2', 3', 4', 5', 6' ; draw the developed length of *B' C'* on springing line '(which is also equal to *C' D'* and is half of the inside face) from *C* to *D'* ; transfer 1', 2', 3', 4',

E

5', 6' from Fig. 1, and draw the ordinates of equal height to those of Fig. 2, cutting Fig. 3 at 1^a, 2^a, 3^a, 4^a, &c., through the points 1^a, 2^a, 3^a, 4^a, &c.; draw the half of semi-ellipse, which gives the curve of the arris to the soffit.

The length of the joints in Fig. 3 is determined in the same manner as in Fig. 2—namely, by means of ordinates.   One joint is here given as an example:

From A No. 2 A (Fig. 2) drop a perpendicular cutting the springing line at 2 C; and from 2 C to 2 transfer to 2 C and 2 on the segment line of plan (Fig. 1), and draw radiating lines from 2 C to the centre O, cutting the segment A' C' at 2 d; transfer the distance from 2 d to 2' on to the springing line (Fig. 3).   Set up ordinate and make equal in height to a on Fig. 2, and from 2 A to A' (Fig. 3) draw joint line, which also radiates from the centre C.

The moulds required for working each arch block are a bed mould and two face moulds (one to the convex and one to the concave face); these are already set out on plan and in developed elevations, but now require separating.

As an example, No. 1 A (Fig. 2) is the springer.   For the bed mould take A B 2 and A' B' 2' from plan (Fig. 1), and transfer to 1 C (Fig. 4).

The dotted line B B' shews the line of the soffit on the bottom bed, the line a a' the line of the arch joint on the top bed, A A' the line of radiating vertical joint, and 2 2' the line of arris of the arch joint.   This gives the plan of a segment of a hollow cylinder to the extreme size of the stone.

No. 1 A (Fig. 4) is the face mould for convex face, No. 1 B (Fig. 4) is the face mould for concave face, and both of these are transferred from 1 A and 1 B (Figs. 2 and 3) with the addition of the square line 2 2 and 2' 2'.

The stone for the arch block should be large enough to work the bed mould square through; if there is a " wanty " corner in the rough block, this may be arranged for in the corner where the stone has to be cut away for the soffit or the top joint.

Work the two beds bottom and top parallel to each other and of the height of the face mould, scribe in the bed mould No. 1 C on both beds (to be correct this should be boned in), the vertical joint A d being at right angles to the bed.   Next work the convex and concave faces through, and also the radiating joint A A', the block at this stage being a portion of a hollow cylinder similar to sketch (Fig. 7).

PLATE. XX.

ARCHES *CIRCULAR ON PLAN*

DEVELOPMENTS

HALF CONVEX *(OUTSIDE)* — HALF CONCAVE *(INSIDE)*

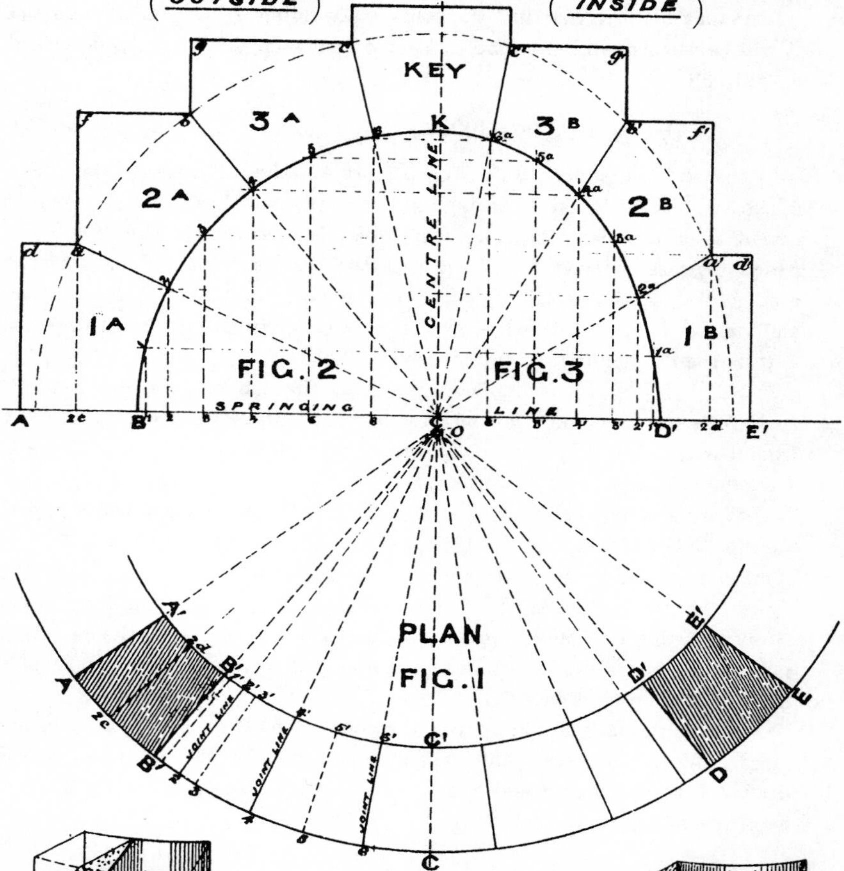

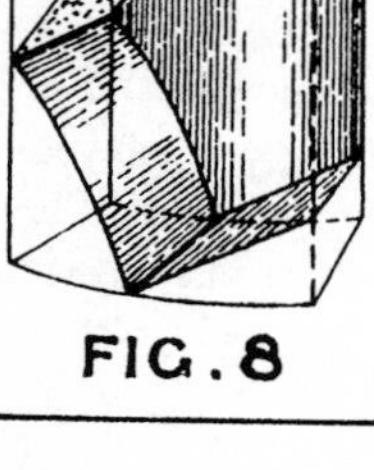

KEY

3 A   K   3 B

2 A   2 B

1 A   1 B

FIG. 2   CENTRE LINE   FIG. 3

A   2e   B'   SPRINGING   O   LINE   D'   2d   E'

PLAN
FIG. I

FIG. 8 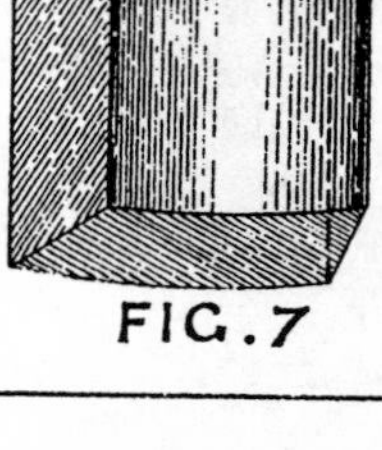   FIG. 7

Now scribe in the face moulds 1 *A* on the convex and 1 *B* on the concave faces (Fig. 4); next work the arch joint *a e* through (this will have a slight twist); and, lastly, for the soffit cut in a draft *B e* on convex and *B' e'* on concave faces, and work the surface through, thus completing the springer.

It may be observed that the soffit is a winding or warped surface, and it will be worked similar to the soffit of winder step, as previously described on page 38.

To work the Second Arch Stone, No. 2 A (*Fig.* 2).

For the bed mould 2 *C* (Fig. 5), project the extreme points *a* and 4, No. 2 *A* (Fig. 2) on to springing line; transfer these to the segment line *A C* on the plan (Fig. 1). This gives from 2 *C* to 4 and 2 *d* to 4', which encloses the bed mould; *a a'* is the vertical joint and arris of the arch joint *a* 2, the dotted line 2 2^a is the horizontal line of the joint on soffit at bottom, and the line *b b'* is the arris at the top of arch joint, 4 4*a* is the bottom arris of the top joint to soffit.

No. 2 *A* (Fig. 5), is the face mould for the convex face, and No. 2 *B* (Fig. 5) is the face mould for the concave face; both of these are transferred from 2 *A* and 2 *B* (Figs. 2 and 3), with the addition of the square line 4 *b*, 4 *C*, and 4 1, 4 2.

Work the top bed first *f b*, 4 *b*, and take the bottom bed *a* 2, 4 *C* parallel to the top and of the height of the face mould (this is a surface of operation, all being cut away except arris 2 2 *a*, which must be kept true across the bed). Scribe the bed mould No. 2 *C* (Fig. 5) on both beds. Now work the two faces convex and concave through, and the radiating joint *a a'* square with the top bed, bringing it again into the shape of a portion of hollow cylinder, as in sketch (Fig. 7).

Scribe the face mould 2 *A* on the convex and 2 *B* (Fig. 5) on concave faces. Work the arch joints *a* 2 and *b* 4, and for the soffit cut in the draft 2 4 on the convex and 2 *a*, 4 *a* on concave faces, and work through as previously described.

The other arch stone 3 *A* and keystone are worked in a similar manner, the general principles of working being the same.

Note.—The radiating joint lines on the developments (Figs. 2 and 3) to be geometrically correct should not be straight, being slightly curved. This is apparent on cutting a cylinder by a right line obliquely, the development of which is a compound curve; but in this case the curve is so

PLATE. XXI.

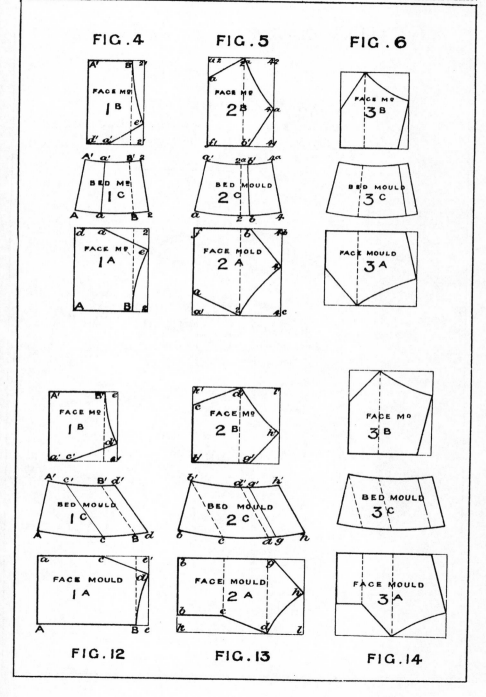

PLATE. XXII.

ARCHES CIRCULAR ON PLAN

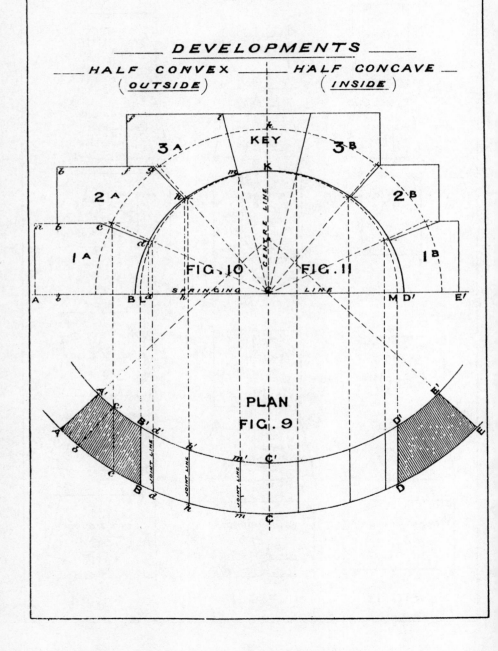

DEVELOPMENTS

HALF CONVEX ——— HALF CONCAVE
(OUTSIDE) (INSIDE)

KEY

3A   3B

2A   2B

1A   1B

FIG. 10   FIG. 11

SPRINGING   LINE

PLAN
FIG. 9

slight as to be scarcely perceptible, and need not in the present and the following example be taken notice of.

To construct a SEMI-CIRCULAR ARCH in a CYLINDRICAL WALL, whose line of soffit on the plan is parallel to the axis, the axes of the two cylinders intersecting each other at right angles.

Fig. 9.—Shews the plan of the arch, *B C D* being the opening.

Figs. 10 and 11 are the developed elevations.

In order to prevent confusion with Figs. 9, 10, and 11, and to make matters easier of explanation, three diagrams are here shewn containing Fig. 15, Figs. 16, 17, and Figs. 18, 19, these being slightly exaggerated to shew more clearly the working.

Let Fig. 15 be the plan of segment of cylinder, with the semi-cylinder penetrating the same at right angles to the axis at *a e, b d*.

Let Fig. 16 be the square section of the quadrant of cylinder, and divide this into any unequal number of equal parts corresponding to the number of arch stones required in Figs. 10 and 11, which in this example is seven, as 1, 2, 3, 4, 5, 6, 7, and project on to the segment line *a c b* on plan (Fig. 15), as *C* 6, 5, 4, 3, 2, 1 ; transfer this to the springing line *a b*, 1, 2, 3, 4, 5, 6, 7 (Fig. 17), which is now the developed line ; erect ordinates, and make them equal in height to the ordinates of the square section, as 1′, 2′, 3′, 4′, &c. ; draw line through the intersecting points 1′, 2′, 3′, 4′, &c., giving the curve required on the development at the point of penetration for the outside or convex face of cylinder.

For the development of the inside or concave face, let Fig: 18 be the square section, divided into seven equal parts, projecting the ordinates as before. Transfer from Fig. 15 1ᵃ, 2ᵃ, 3ᵃ, 4ᵃ, 5ᵃ, 6ᵃ, 7ᵃ to the springing line (Fig. 19), erect ordinates and make them equal in height to those of square section at 1, 2, 3, 4, &c., and through the intersecting points 1ᵃ, 2ᵃ, 3ᵃ, 4ᵃ, &c., draw the line giving curve required at the point of penetration for the inside or concave face of cylinder.

For the joints, draw radiating lines at 2, 4, 6 (Figs. 16 and 18), and to make them of equal length draw a quadrant line with radius of the square section as *f g h*, project *f g h* on to plan (Fig. 15) as *f g h*, and transfer to the springing line (Figs. 17 and 19) ; erect ordinates at *f g h*, making equal in height to those of the square section. Next draw the joint lines *h* 2′,

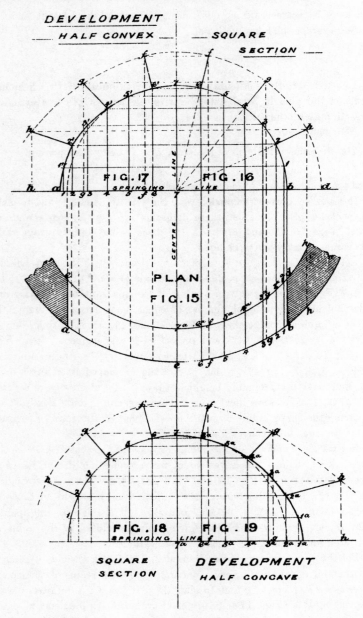

PLATE. XXIII.

ARCHES *CIRCULAR ON PLAN*

DEVELOPMENT

HALF CONVEX · SQUARE

SECTION

FIG. 17 · FIG. 16

SPRINGING LINE

PLAN

FIG. 15

FIG. 18 · FIG. 19

SPRINGING LINE

SQUARE
SECTION

DEVELOPMENT

HALF CONCAVE

g 4´, *f c'* on Fig. **17**, and *h* 2ᵃ, *g* 4ᵃ, and *f cᵃ* (Fig. **19**) ; the developed
length of joint is thus obtained.

To set up the Elevation on the Developments for the Face Moulds.

Figs. 10 and 11.—Let *A E'* be the springing line, *C K* the centre
line, and *L K M* dotted line the square section of the cylinder whose centre
is *C.* For the development *B K D* proceed as previously described, and
divide into any number of equal parts for the arch stones required—which
in this example is seven—and draw the joints ; the square bonding *a b, b f,
f l* may be set out at will, but should be set out from the inside or concave
face, so as to obtain a parallel arch joint.

The joint *c b'*, No. 2 *C* (Fig. **13**), which is the arch joint cutting out to
the vertical joint *b'*, illustrates this.

The moulds for working each arch block are a bed mould and two face
moulds. These are already set out on plan (Fig. 9) and elevations (Figs. 10
and 11), except the addition of a square line to the extreme size.

To work the springer :

For the bed mould take *A c, B d* from the plan (Fig. 9) and transfer to
1 *C* (Fig. 12) ; the dotted line *B B'* is line of the soffit on the bottom bed,
the line *c c'* is the line of joint on top bed, the line *d d'* is the line of
arris of the arch joint in soffit, and the line *A A'* is the radiating vertical
joint. No. 1 *A* (Fig. 12) is the face mould for convex face, and No. 1 *B*,
Fig. 12, is the face mould for concave face ; both of these are transferred
from 1 *A* and 1 *B* (Figs. 10 and 11), with the addition of the square
line *e e'*.

Work the two beds (bottom and top) parallel to each other, and of the
height of the face mould. Scribe the bed mould No. 1 *C* (Fig. 12), on both
beds, and work the two faces convex and concave through, and also the
vertical joint *A a*, which must be at right angles to beds ; this will form a
portion of a hollow cylinder similar to sketch Fig. 7. Now scribe in the
face moulds 1 *A* and 1 *B* (Fig. 12), on the convex and concave faces respectively, and work the arch joint *c d* through and for the soffit, cut in
arrises to the lines, and work drafts parallel to the bed *B B'* until the
whole of the soffit is finished.

In this arch the soffit is not a winding surface.

To work the Second Arch Stone No. 2 *A (Fig.* 10).

Let No. 2 *C* (Fig. 13) be the bed mould, project the extreme points *b h*, No. 2 *A* (Fig. 10), on to springing line *A C*. This being a developed face it will require folding back on to the segment line *A C E* of plan (Fig. 9), as *b d h*, and transfer this to No. 2 *C*, which gives the bed mould.

No. 2 *A* (Fig. 13) is the face mould for convex face, and No. 2 *B* (Fig. 13) is the face mould for concave face, and both of these are transferred from 2 *A* and 2 *B* (Figs. 10 and 11), with the addition of the square line *l*.

Work the two beds (bottom and top) parallel to each other, and to the height of the face mould. The bottom bed is worked as a surface of operation for the application of the bed mould, and it is all cut away except the arris *d d'*. Scribe the bed mould 2 *C* (Fig. 13) in on each bed, and work the two faces convex and concave through, and scribe in the face moulds 2 *A* and 2 *B* (Fig. 13).

Work the vertical joint *b b* square with either the top or bottom beds, and work the bed *b c* and joint *c d*; then joint *g h*, and, lastly, soffit *d h*.

Fig. 14.—Nos. 3 *A*, 3 *B*, and 3 *C* are the face moulds and bed mould of the third arch stone, and together with the keystone are projected and worked in precisely the same manner as the foregoing Nos. 1 and 2 stones.

It will be advisable for the student to work small models, which should be constructed to scale in plaster, clay, or other soft material. The moulds for these models may be cut out of stout drawing paper, and in their application will be found the best method of obtaining knowledge of these subjects.

PLATE. XXIV.

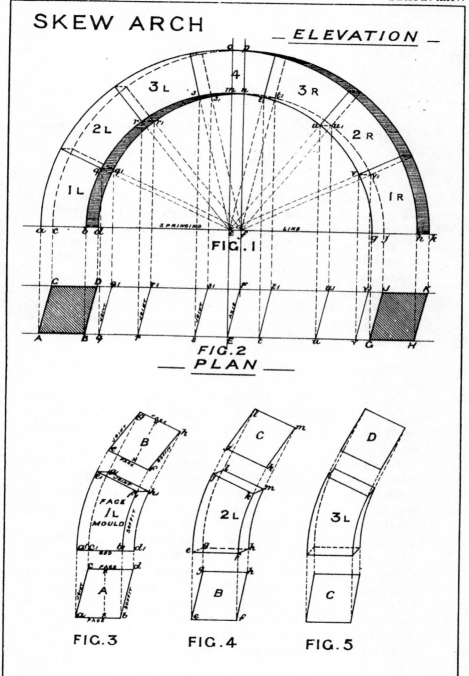

SKEW ARCH

ELEVATION

FIG. 1

FIG. 2

PLAN

FIG. 3

FIG. 4

FIG. 5

Plates XXIV., XXV., XXVI.—SKEW ARCH AND NICHES.

To construct a Semi-circular Arch Rib, the oblique angle of which does not extend more than ten or twelve degrees from a right angle, the joints being parallel to axis, and in the same planes.

This is not a difficult problem, as the arch within these limits may be set out and worked as a right arch; but beyond these a different principle of construction is necessary.

The archivolt and arch ribs to coffered vaulting at the entrance to Burlington House, Piccadilly (about 20 feet span), and the archivolt at entrance to the Criterion Restaurant, Piccadilly, which are similar to the above, were set out by the writer, and worked as herein described.

Fig. 1.—Shews the elevation of the arch, which is a semi-circle.

Fig. 2.—Shews the plan of the arch, $B\ G$ and $D\ J$ being the opening, $B\ D$ and $G\ J$ the inclination or angle of skew, E and F the centres, A and H the outer face line of the arch, and $C\ K$ the inner face line of the arch.

There is no difference in the outer and inner faces of the arch, both being alike, but the terms are here used for purpose of explanation.

Project $A\ C$, $B\ D$ and $G\ J$, $H\ K$ from the plan to the springing line (Fig. 1), as $a\ c$, $b\ d$ and $g\ j$, $h\ k$, with e as centre, and $e\ a$ and $e\ b$ as radius, describe the semi-circles $a\ o\ h$ and $b\ m\ g$, for the outside face, and with f as centre, and the same radius, describe the semi-circles $c\ p\ k$ and $d\ n\ j$, for the inside face. For the joints, divide the arch into any convenient number of equal parts—in this example seven—as $q\ r\ s\ t\ u\ v$ on line $b\ m\ g$ of intrados, and with the same divisions repeat on the line $d\ n\ j$ as $q'\ r'\ s'\ t'\ u'\ v'$; from the centre e draw radiating lines through these points, and produce to the outside curve or extrados for the outside, and for the inside of the arch; repeat the same from the centre f. It will be observed that the direction of joints is perfectly horizontal, the lines $q\,q'$, $r\,r'$, $s\,s'$, &c., being level; the radiating lines and joints are also parallel to each other, and are therefore in the same plane.

This is all the setting out required, with the exception of the joint moulds.

To work the Arch Stones.

Fig. 3.—Let No. 1 L be the face mould of the springer and A and B the joint moulds.

The face mould 1 L, is transferred from the elevation Fig. 1, and the bottom bed or joint mould A, from plan (Fig. 2); for the joint mould B, draw a line parallel to joint $e'\,f'$, and project $e'\,f'$ and $g'\,h'$ as $e\,f$ and $g\,h$, of an equal and parallel thickness, as $X\,X$ at A and B.

Work $a'\,b'\,e'\,f'$ outside face of springer No. 1 L, to a plane surface, and $c\,d\,g\,h$ inside, face parallel to it; scribe the face mould in to extreme size on each face as $a'\,d'\,e'\,g'\,h'$; scribe in the segment line $f'\,b'$ giving arris of soffit on outside face (this may be done by drawing the mould back, as $h'\,d'$ is the same segment and also the same length as $f'\,b'$).

Work the bottom bed A which is horizontal, and square with the vertical face, and scribe in the bed mould as $a\,b\,c\,d$, which will coincide with the lines on the face mould: now work the top joint B, this from the outside face will be full of the square, or, in other words, it makes an obtuse angle with the vertical face. This, however, is given by the face mould, as $e'\,f'$ is line of joint on the outside, and $g'\,h'$ on the inside.

Scribe in the joint mould B as $e\,f\,g\,h$, and work the soffit $b'\,d'\,f'\,h'$ through, as in a right arch, and finish with the back joint $a'\,c'\,e'\,g'$.

Fig. 4.—No. 2 L is worked similar to No. 1 L; the top joint mould B of No. 1 is the bottom joint mould of No. 2, and the top joint mould C of No. 2 is the bottom joint mould of No. 3, and so on,—this is self evident. The bevels of these joints are found by projecting the points of the face mould, as $j\,k\,l\,m$, &c., as before described.

Begin by working the two vertical faces $e\,f\,j\,k$ and $g\,h\,l\,m$ parallel to each other, scribe in the face mould No. 2 to the extreme size as $e\,f\,h\,j\,l\,m$, and work both joints B and C; the top joint C is full of the square, whilst the bottom joint B is slack of the square from the outside face, the amount of the obtuse and acute angle being given on the face mould.

Fig. 5.—No. 3 L and the key-stone are worked precisely similar to the foregoing.

One set of moulds for one half of the arch only is required, as the four face moulds and the four joint moulds will work the complete arch:

being a plain arch without mouldings, the stones are reversible; this is apparent on looking at the elevation, but should there be an architrave moulding on one face, a mould to each stone is then required.

To construct a SPHERICAL NICHE in a straight wall with horizontal splay beds, and with vertical joints.

Figs. 6 and 7.—Shew the elevation and plan of the niche.

Let $A E$ be the face line of the niche on plan (Fig. 7), $B D$ the opening and C the centre; with $C B$ or $C D$ as radius, and C as centre, describe a semi-circle $B K D$, which is plan of extreme size of inside of niche; project $A B C D E$ to the springing line on elevation (Fig. 6), as $a b c d e$, and at c erect perpendicular for the centre line. With c as centre and $c b$ or $c d$ as radius, describe the semi-circle $b k d$ for the outer curve, and divide this into five equal parts as at $f g h i$; from c draw radiating lines through these points of division, cutting the horizontal bed at $l m n o$, giving the joints, the bevel of which will be continued horizontally round the niche as at $f i$ and $g h$. For joints to the plan draw ordinates at $f g h i$ and $l m$, &c., and project them on to line $A E$ on plan (Fig. 7), as $F G H I$ and $L M$, &c.; at $L F M G$ describe the semi-circles, giving the horizontal line of splay joints. For dividing joints on the plan, take the second course first and divide the line of semi-circle $F Q I$ into four equal parts as $P Q R$, and from C draw radiating lines through these divisions, producing them on to the line $L N O$, which gives the joints. The springers 1 L and 1 R in the first course will require to be about half the depth of others in the same course, in order to break the bond (as will be seen by reference to the plan); therefore, on the line $B K D$, set off say little more than half for the two springers as $B S$ and $D V$, dividing the remainder into three equal parts as at $S T U V$, and draw the lines through, radiating from the centre to the back, giving the joints in the bottom course.

The top course No. 3 is in one stone, and to prevent any tendency to slip out of its place forward, the upper part of bed may be kept square; this would require notching on the inside, as $M M 2$ and $N M 2$ on the plan, and $m 4 4$ and $n 5 5$ on the elevation.

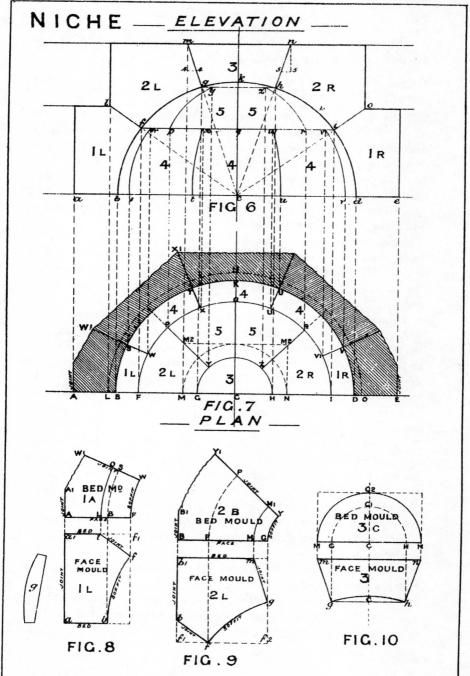

PLATE. XXV.

The vertical joints are shewn on the elevation by projecting up from the plan, as shewn by the dotted lines *w p x q,* &c.

To work the Springer.

Fig. 8.—1 *A* is the bed mould transferred from the plan (Fig. 7), the line *A F* being the vertical. face on the front, *F W* the horizontal line of arris of soffit and splay joint on the top bed, *L O* the outside line of splay joint on top bed, the dotted line *B S* the line of soffit on bottom bed, *W W'* the line of vertical radiating joint, and *A A'* the line of vertical face joint.

1 *L* is the face mould transferred from the elevation (Fig. 6), which will also apply as joint mould at *W W'*

The form of the stone required to work this will be a wedge-shape prism, containing the bed mould to the extreme size on the top bed as *A F W W'* ; the bottom bed is a little smaller, and is contained within the lines *A B S W'*, and of the extreme height of the face mould from *a* to *a'.*

Begin by working the front vertical face *A B F*, and scribe the face mould 1 *L* on, as *a b f l a'.* Work the vertical joint *A A'* as *a a'* square with the front face, and bottom and top beds square with the front face, scribing on the bed mould 1 *A*, and also the inside vertical joint *W W'*, scribing in the face mould as *a b f l a'.* It is necessary to work the whole of the top bed, although a portion from *l* to *f* 1 will be cut away for the splay joint, in order to get horizontal line *F W* at *f*; to obtain this arris, square down the concave line from *F* to *W* to the depth at *f*, or a draft from *F* to *W*, may be worked by the aid of a templet. This being done, trammel the line *f* parallel to *f* 1, giving the arris line required; the line *L O* is marked on the top bed with the templet, and the splay joint from *f* to *l* then worked off. The soffit now remains to be worked : cut in the drafts *B S* on the bottom bed and *F W* on the top bed, and drafts *b f* on the face and joint ; a convex templet is used as at *g* for the intermediate drafts, which are cut in as close as convenient, until the whole surface is worked.

The templet *g* must not be applied parallel to the joints, but to lines radiating from the centre.

The three No. 4 stones will be worked similarly to the foregoing ; one vertical joint is worked first as a surface of operation, instead of the front face as in the springer.

PLATE. XXVI

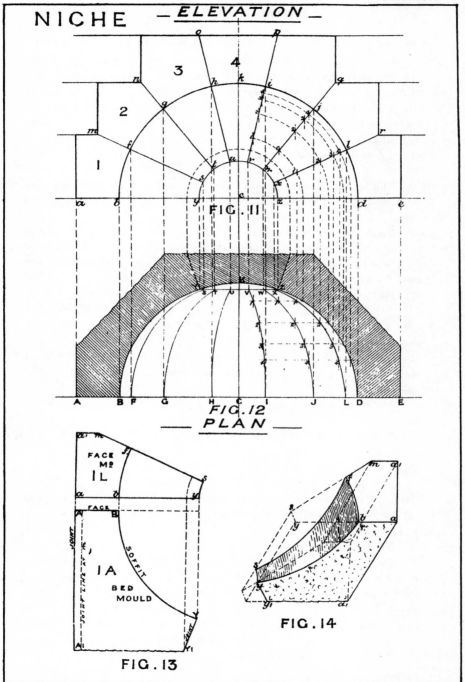

NICHE — ELEVATION —

FIG. 11

FIG. 12

— PLAN —

FIG. 13

FIG. 14

To work No. 2 L Stone.

Fig. 9.—2 B is the bed mould transferred from the plan (Fig. 7), the line $B G$ being the vertical face on the front, and $G Y$ the horizontal line of the arris of soffit and the splay joint on the top bed, $M M'$ the outside line of the splay joint top bed, the dotted line $F P$ the line of soffit on bottom bed, $Y Y'$ the line of vertical radiating joint, and $B B'$ the line of vertical face joint.

2 L is the face mould, transferred from the elevation (Fig. 6), which will also apply as joint mould at $Y Y'$.

The form of stone required to work this will be a wedge-shape prism, containing the bed mould, to the extreme size as $B G Y Y 1$, and of the extreme height of the face mould, from $f 1$ to $b 1$.

Begin by working the front vertical face, and scribe the face mould 2 L on as $b 1 b f g m$. Work the vertical joint $b b'$ square with the front face, also the top bed, and scribe the bed mould on. Work the bottom bed as a surface of operation; the only part required being the arris of the splay joint, and soffit $F P$, the rest of the bed being cut away.

This is the easiest and most accurate way of working, but the bed need not necessarily be worked as a whole, a portion only being required, sufficient to obtain the arris line $F P$; in this case the soffit $F G$ should be worked after the arris line is drawn on the bed, by a convex templet made from f to g, and the splay joint is worked from a bevelled templet made from $g f b$.

The remaining portion of the stone is worked as before described to springer.

The two No. 5 stones are worked similarly.

To work the Key-stone No. 3.

Fig. 10.—3 C is the bed mould transferred from the plan (Fig. 7), the line $M N$ being the vertical face on the front, $M C 2 N$ the top line of the splay joint, and $G C 1 H$ the line of arris of soffit, and the splay joint on bottom.

No. 3 is the face mould transferred from the elevation (Fig. 6).

Begin by working the vertical face $M N$, scribing in the face mould as $g h m n$. Work the top bed through square with the face, scribing in the bed mould, also the bottom bed parallel to the top at extreme points g and h, and with a templet scribe $G C H$ the arris of the soffit and the splay joint. Work the joint round to the splay lines, then the soffit by cutting in the draft $g c h$ on the front, and with a convex templet made from C to $C 1$, complete the surface.

The niche need not be jointed as here shewn, for much depends on its size, and the size of the stone convenient to use, but the general principle of working will be the same.

To construct a SPHERICAL NICHE in a straight wall, with joints radiating from the centre.

Figs. 11 and 12.—Shew elevation and plan of the niche.

Let A E be the vertical face line of the niche on the plan (Fig. 12), B D the opening, and C the centre. With C B or C D as a radius, and C as a centre, describe the semi-circle B K D, which is the plan of extreme size of the inside of niche, and project A B C D E to the springing line a e on the elevation (Fig. 11), as a b c d e. At c erect a perpendicular for the centre line, and, with c as centre and c b or c d as radius, describe the semi-circle b k d for the outer curve. With c y as a radius and c as the centre, describe a semi-circle for the centre stone, which may be of any convenient size. Divide the semi-circle b k d into seven equal parts as f g h i j l, and through these points of division from c draw radiating lines cutting horizontal beds at m n o p, &c., and the centre stone at s t u v, &c., which gives the joints. Draw ordinates from f g h i, &c., and project on to the line A B as F G H I, &c., and repeat the same at s t u v, &c., on the line Y Z, giving joint lines on the plan : to determine points in the curve of the soffit for templets, the dotted lines at the right hand of the niche shews how they are obtained. The dotted segment line from 1 to 1, 2 to 2, 3 to 3, &c., on elevation will be the section of curve at corresponding points on the plan at 1 1, 2 2, 3 3, &c., and also gives the points in the line of curve for the joints on plan, although the last named is not necessary for the setting out or the working.

To work the Springer 1 L.

Fig. 13.—1 A is the bed or joint mould transferred from the plan (Fig. 12), the line A B being the front vertical face, B Y the line of soffit, Y Y 1 the splay joint, and A A 1 the vertical face joint.

No. 1 L is the face mould transferred from the elevation (Fig. 11).

The form of stone required will be that of a wedge-shape prism (as in sketch, Fig. 14), containing the face mould to the extreme size as a' a y s m.

Begin by working the bed or joint a b y, keeping the segmental line

B Y fair for arris, and scribe the bed mould 1 *A* on. Work the vertical face and scribe in the face mould 1 *L*, and the other bed *m f s*, scribing in the bed mould 1 *A*. Work the vertical joint *a a'*, and top bed *a' m*, and lastly, the soffit, the working of this being guided by one or two templets made from 1 1, 2 2, &c.

The remaining stones are worked similar to the foregoing, keeping in mind the principle that the stone is contained within the wedge-shape prism, thus making it easy of comprehension.

PLATE. XXVII

FIG. 1

FIG. 2

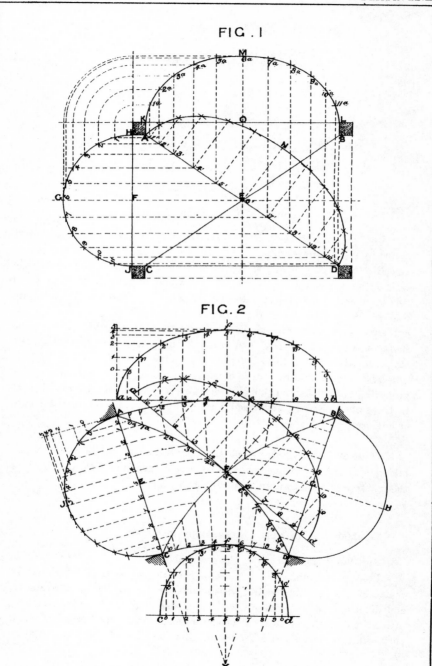

Plates XXVII., XXVIII, XXIX.— CYLINDRICAL VAULTING.

To obtain the Profiles or Curvature of a Groin.

Fig. 1.—Let A B C D be a rectangular plan, its vault to be intersected by two semi-cylinders.

Bisect the line $H J$, and with F as a centre, describe the semi-circle $G H J$ (the given section), which divide into any number of equal parts in this example 12, and project ordinates 1 2 3 4 5, &c., through the springing line $H F J$ on to the diagonal line $A E D$ as $1'$ $2'$ $3'$ $4'$ $5'$, &c. Erect ordinates perpendicular to the diagonal, and make them equal in height to those of semi-circle $G H J$, and through the points of intersection draw the semi-ellipse, which is the curve of the groin.

The outer profile $K L M$ is obtained in the same manner, namely, by projecting ordinates from the diagonal, and making them of equal height to those of semi-circle, and tracing semi-elliptic curve through the points of intersection.

These profiles may also be obtained by means of an elliptic trammel, taking $A D$ and $K L$ respectively as the major axes, and $E N$ and $M O$ as the minor axes, and drawing semi-ellipses by a continuous curve.

To obtain the Profiles for the Annular Groin.

Fig. 2.—Let A B C D be the given plan.

Produce $A C$ and $B D$ until they meet in the point X, which is the centre of the radiating vault; bisect the line $A C$ and $B D$ at E and G, and describe the two semi-circles $A J C$ and $B D H$ the given section; divide the diameter of either semi-circle as $A C$ into any number of equal parts—in this example 10—the last division from 1 to A and 9 to C may be again divided as at O, and erect ordinates as O 1 2 3 4 5, &c., cutting the semi-circle at O' 1' 2' 3' 4' 5', &c.; at the centre X, with radius O 1 2 3 4 5, &c. on the diameter A C, describe concentric arcs to the diameter B D. Divide the segmental line A 5 B into the same number of equal parts as the diameter A C, as O 1 2 3 4 5, &c., and from these points draw radiating lines from centre X, intersecting the above arcs at O^a 1^a 2^a 3^a 4^a 5^a, &c., and through the points of intersection draw the curve, giving the plan of groins A F D and C F B.

To describe the outer and inner profiles, develop segmental line A 5 B as right line a b, and C f D as right line c d, and transfer the divisions O 1 2 3 4 5, &c.; erect ordinates as O' 1' 2' 3' 4' 5', &c., equal in height to those of the semi-circle A J C, and through the points O' 1' 2' 3' 4' 5', &c., draw the curve which gives the true sections.

To find the profile on the diagonals A F D and C F B, develop line A F D as right line a F d, and transfer divisions O^a 1^a 2^a 3^a 4^a 5^a, &c. on the same, erect ordinates, and make them equal in height to those of the semi-circle A J C; through the points of intersection draw the curve, giving the true section at the mitre of groins, when bent or worked, so as to stand on the curve A F D on the plan.

To construct a RECTANGULAR VAULT, intersected by two semi-cylinders, crossing each other at right angles, and of equal height, each course of Stone being level and parallel to the axes of the Cylinders.

Fig. 3.—Let A B C D be the springing of the groins, A E D and C E B plan of the groins or intersection of cylindric surfaces, F H G is a section of the soffit or intrados whose profile is a semi-circle, and I K J a section of the outside or extrados, both of which are concentric semi-circles. The form of this section determines the shape of the groin and outer profile. L M N and O P Q are sections respectively of the intrados and extrados of the semi-elliptic profile, the curves of which are found by the method described in Fig. 1.

To obtain the joints, divide the semi-circle I J K into any unequal number of equal parts (convenient to the size of the stones), in this example 18, and draw the arch joints radiating from the centre R as a' b' c' d' e' f', &c. From the joints on the soffit, as a b c d e f, &c., project lines on to the plan, cutting the diagonal line A $E - C$ E at a b c d e f, &c.; and, from these points of intersection, project lines on to the semi-ellipse L M N for intrados, and project points from the extrados I J, to the

PLATE. XXVIII.

VAULTING _ CYLINDRICAL

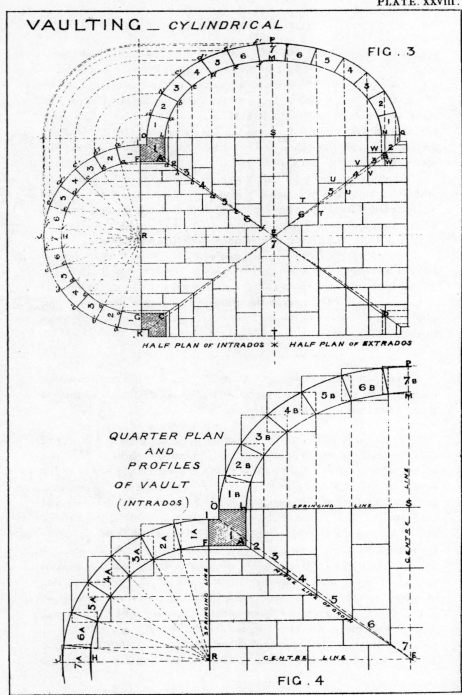

FIG. 3

HALF PLAN OF INTRADOS ✳ HALF PLAN OF EXTRADOS

QUARTER PLAN
AND
PROFILES
OF VAULT
(INTRADOS)

FIG. 4

PLATE. XXIX

VAULTING — *CYLINDRICAL*
FIG . 10

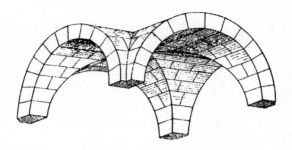

SKETCH OF VAULT

FIG . 5

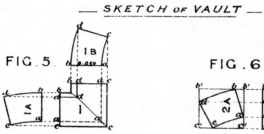

FIG . 6.

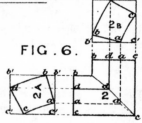

FIG. 5A

FIG. 6A

FIG . 6 B

FIG . 9

FIG. 7A

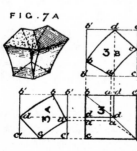

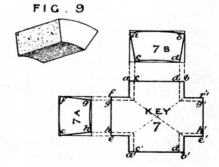

FIG . 7

FIG . 8

extrados $O\ P$, and draw the joint lines through, which gives the direction and position of joints.

The vertical cross joints in vault may be drawn at pleasure, care being taken to "bond" by breaking joint, but the angle quoins of the groin must be treated differently, and for this reason : the extrados of the arch is set out on the plan as shewn on the right hand half, and; by noting the joints 3 4 5 6 at $T\ U\ V\ W$, it will be observed that the vertical joints of the groins are set out to the mitre, which governs the size on the soffit. If the stones were set out less than this there would not be so good a bed, as this size should be the minimum.

The dotted diagonal lines on the half plan of the intrados shew the mitre on the extrados, and the dotted diagonal lines on the half plan of the extrados shew the mitre of the groin on the intrados. Although the extrados is here shewn apparently as a finished face, yet in practice it is not so, as it is generally left rough, and stepped out as a seating for concrete.

The stones which present any difficulty in the working in this form of vault are the angular groins, and these are the weakest part of the vault, on account of each stone acting to some extent as a corbel, and one corbel standing upon another, as indicated by the sketch (Fig. 10). Therefore care must be taken in working them true to shape and form.

The stones in other portion of the vault may be worked as those in a right arch.

The easiest way of working either of the groin stones is to take a block cubical in form, and containing it, as shewn in Fig. 6 B ; and, although in stones No. 3, 4 and 5, there is a little waste attached to this method, yet it gives the best results, and is more correct in shape when worked than by using bevels. The danger of using bevels is in the application of them, that is to say, should there be the least deviation from the actual position in applying the bevel, the stone would not be true. This would not be of so much consequence were it an isolated block, but where it is surrounded by others, and forming a cylindric surface, it is of importance.

Fig. 4.—Shews a quarter plan and profiles of the vault to a larger scale, for the purpose of shewing more clearly the working of the groins ;

in actual work this is all that is necessary to set out, as the set of moulds of one groin will work the three others if "handed," that is worked in pairs.

Fig. 5.—Is the springing stone. No. 1 is the bed mould, 1 *A* and 1 *B* the joint moulds.

Begin by working the bottom bed, this being horizontal, and scribe on the bed mould; next work the two vertical faces or joints *c a d b*, and scribe in the joint moulds 1 *A* and 1 *B*, then the top splay joint *c d*, and lastly the curved soffit, care being taken to keep the mitre true.

Fig. 5A.—Shews a sketch of this stone finished; the working of this differs very little from that of an ordinary arch stone.

Fig. 6.—Is the second stone. No. 2 is the bed mould, and 2 *A* and 2 *B* the joint moulds.

Work the two beds parallel to each other, and of the extreme height of the joint mould from *a* to *d*, as surfaces of operation; labour need not be thrown away on these beds, as they may be roughly chiselled over and at the same time true: the mason should know just where to put the work that is necessary, in some cases, perhaps, a couple or three straight drafts being all that is required. This done, scribe in the bed mould No. 1 on the bottom and top bed. Work the vertical joints *c a d b*, scribing in the joint moulds 2 *A* and 2 *B*. The position of these moulds is given by the circumscribing rectangle, coinciding with the lines on the bed mould; next work the splay beds, and then the curved soffit guided by a convex templet, keeping the mitre also true.

Fig. 6A.—Shews a sketch of the stone when finished.

Fig. 6B.—Shews a sketch of the same contained within the circumscribing prism.

Fig. 7.—Is the third stone. This is worked precisely as the last named in Fig. 6.

Fig. 7A.—Shews a sketch of this stone when finished.

Fig. 8.—Is the key-stone No. 7.

In working this stone commence on the soffit plane, the points $a\ b$ and $e\ f$ and points opposite these being in this plane, which may be taken as a surface of operation. Scribe in the bed mould No. 7; the dotted lines $c\ d$ and $g\ h$ shew the finished arris on the soffit. Work the two joints $a\ b$ and the two joints $e\ f$ at right angles to the plane, and scribe in the joint moulds 7 A and 7 B, then the splay joints $a\ c$—$f\ g$, &c., and lastly the concave surfaces $c\ d$ and $g\ h$. The mitres of intersection being here very obtuse must be carefully worked.

Fig. 9.—Shews a sketch of one of the ordinary arch stones between the groins, which is worked similar to that of a right arch.

Fig. 10.—Shews a sketch of the vault.

PLATE. XXX.

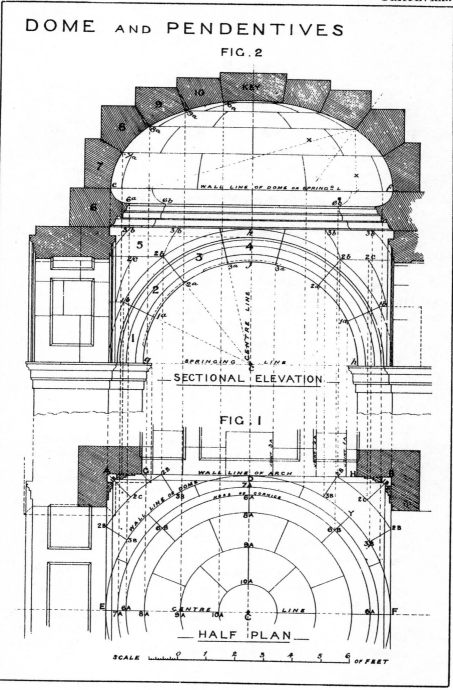

DOME AND PENDENTIVES

FIG. 2

SECTIONAL ELEVATION

FIG 1

HALF PLAN

SCALE 0 1 2 3 4 5 6 OF FEET

Plates XXX., XXXI., XXXII., XXXIII.—DOMES AND PENDENTIVES.

The DOME may be generally described as a convex roof or vault, covering a circular elliptical or polygonal area.

The PENDENTIVES are the corbellings resting on the internal angles of piers, and support the dome.

Fig. 1A.—If a hemisphere or other portion of a sphere, *a b a*, be intersected by vertical planes, *a d c*, equidistant from its centre, the angular or spandril portion, *e e*, between the boundaries of the planes are pendentives.

Fig. 1.—Shews half plan of square area, covered by dome and supported by pendentives.

Fig. 2.—Shews sectional elevation of the dome and pendentives, taken through the centre line *E F* on plan.

For the making of the moulds, and working of this vault, a quarter plan only is required to be set out full size; but in order to shew it more clearly the half is here given.

Begin by setting out on the plan (Fig. 1). the rectangle *A B E F*, the line *E F* being the centre line, and the line *C D* being the transverse centre line. The semi-circle *E D F* is the half of inscribed circle, forming wall line of cornice and dome.

Set out the archivolt on impost caps at *A* and *B* as shewn by hatched lines, which gives the span or opening of arches, and project on to springing line of section (Fig. 2).

At *c* as centre, with *c g* or *c h* as radius, describe semi-circle *g j h* for soffit, and semi-circles concentric to this for lines of mouldings forming archivolt. The arch at crown *j k* must equal in height the width at springing A G, Fig. 1, so that the corbelling of pendentives start exactly in the angles at A and B on springing line at top of impost cap.

Divide the arch into any number of equal parts—in this example 7—and draw joints radiating from centre c as 1^a 2^a 3^a &c. ; at extremities of joints as $1 b 2 b$ draw horizontal lines for beds (these are better if worked in conical or splay beds, but as it takes more material they are generally horizontal as shewn at Fig. 3). Project $1 b$, $2 b$ on to wall line of arch on plan, fig. 1, and with C as centre describe arcs $1 B$, $2 B$, giving line of curvature of horizontal joints in pendentive. The vertical joints may be drawn in at will, but are here shewn as at $1 B$, $2 B$, $3 B$.

It will be observed that the arch is panelled on soffit, and is shewn on section by a chamfer, the detail being too small to shew a moulding.

Set up the section of cornice No. 6 and project nosing on to plan (Fig. 1) as $6 A$. For vertical joints divide cornice into 8 parts, this being a convenient number for stones in the dome, and also breaking joint with those in pendentives.

Draw in the joints which radiate from the centre C (Fig. 1) at $6 A$, $6 B$, and project on to the section (Fig. 2).

The wall line of the cornice, $e f$, Fig. 2, is the springing line of dome, and equals the width $E C F$ on centre line of plan (Fig. 1).

On the line $e f$ set up the curvature of dome, which is a semi-ellipse, and may be struck with the trammel or the curve may be traced through points in the inter-section of lines.

For the joints divide the dome into any convenient number—in this example 9—as Nos. 7, 8, 9, 10, &c., and draw radiating lines perpendicular to the tangent of the curve, as at 7^a, 8^a, 9^a, &c. ; see construction as shewn by dotted lines $X X$.

Project 7^a, 8^a, 9^a, &c., on to plan (Fig. 1), and, with C as centre, and $7 A$, $8 A$, $9 A$, &c., as radii, describe semi-circles which give horizontal lines in splay joints of dome.

For the vertical joints follow divisions of joints in cornice, the same number (eight) being required in each course, breaking joint, as shewn on plan and section.

Fig. 3.—Is a section on the centre line, shewing corbelling out of the pendentive taken across the diagonal from B to Y on the plan (Fig. 1), the radius of which equals the distance from C to B, and the projection B', Y' equalling B, Y on the plan (Fig. 1).

PLATE. XXXI

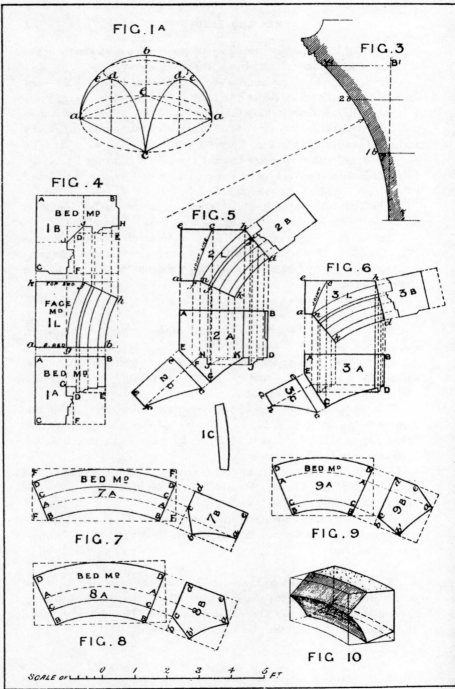

FIG. 1A

FIG. 3

FIG. 4

FIG. 5

FIG. 6

1C

FIG. 7

FIG. 9

FIG. 8

FIG. 10

SCALE OF 0 1 2 3 4 5 FT.

To work the Double Springer No 1.

Fig. 4.—1 *A* is the bottom bed mould, 1 *B* is the top bed mould, and 1 *L* is the face mould.

The stone will require to be cubical in form, and the size of bed mould 1 *B*, and of the height of face mould 1 *L*.

Work the bottom bed and scribe in bed mould 1 *A*; work vertical joints *A B* and *A C* square with the bottom bed, and apply face mould 1 *L* to each joint and scribe in; next take the top bed *k j* parallel to bottom bed. Work out the check *D E F* right through, keeping the nosing of moulding fair or clean, and apply part of face mould 1 *L* coinciding with the moulds marked on vertical joints *A B* and *A C*, which gives the soffit line *h b*, the splay joint *j h* and the nose and mitre line of the archivolt.

Work the splay joints *j h* and scribe in the archivolt, which is part of the bed mould 1 *A*; next the soffits and panels and archivolt mouldings guided by convex templets; lastly, work the small concave portion of pendentive, which starts imperceptibly at the angle *G* on the bottom bed, and increases to *J J* on the top bed.

The convex templet 1 *C* gives the curvature in the centre from *G*—1 *A*, to *D*—1 *B*. An obtuse mitre is formed on each side where the spandrel intersects the archivolt, and is shewn by the segmental line *j g* on the face mould 1 *L*.

It will be observed that the archivolt on the bed mould 1 *B* is foreshortened, but 1 *A*, being a square section, is used on all arch joints.

To work No. 2 Arch Stone.

Fig. 5.—No. 2 *A* is the bed mould, 2 *L* the face mould, 2 *B* the joint mould of arch, and 2 *C* the joint mould of a portion of the pendentive.

This stone will require to be the size of the bed mould, and of the extreme height of the face mould 2 *L* from *k* to *h*.

Begin by working the top bed *e c h*—2 *L*, and scribe in bed mould 2 *A*, as *A B C D E*. Work the vertical joints *A B* and *E C* square with top bed, and scribe in the face mould 2 *L*, and joint mould 2 *C* respectively; point off vertical side *A E*, and rough out section of pendentive *c f* from joint *E C* on to face line *N K*, and work draft through at *J J* for nosing. Apply part of face mould *h d f n k*—2 *L*, coinciding with the face mould marked in on vertical joint *A B*, and work the splay joints *h d*—*n k*, and bottom bed *a n*. Scribe in archivolt mould 2 *B* on joints *h d* and *n k*, and run the moulding through ; clean in portion of pendentive *c f*—2 *C* intersecting with archivolt and forming obtuse mitre on the segment line *n* to *h*, and lastly, work panelled soffit.

Fig. 6.—No. 3 arch stone is worked in a similar manner to the foregoing No. 2 (Fig. 5).

No. 4, the key-stone, needs but little explanation, it being worked similarly to that of a right arch, with the exception of the mitre of the pendentive, which is here very obtuse and loses itself at *k*.

The section mould at each joint is 3 *B* (Fig. 6), taken to the dotted line.

Note.—The dotted lines shew the projection of coinciding points in the face and bed moulds of Figs. 4, 5, and 6.

The section of cornice directly under dome is shewn on Fig. 2, No. 6. A bed mould for this is required and also convex templets for the mouldings and fillets, these are obtained from the plan (Fig. 1), 6 *A* being the nose line. The working of this stone presents no difficulty.

To work the Voussoirs in the Dome.

The shape of stone for working one of these is first, a rectangular prism, of the extreme length of the bed mould 7 *A* (Fig. 7), as shewn by circumscribed dotted lines *F F*, and of the height of joint mould 7 *B*, and second, that of a segment of a hollow cylinder, as shewn in sketch (Fig. 10), which contains the finished block.

Fig. 7.—7 *A* is the bed mould, and 7 *B* the section or joint mould of springer, or first stone in dome.

Begin by working the bottom bed *a e*—7 *B*, and scribe on the bed mould 7 *A*, the dotted line *A A* being the wall line on bottom bed, which must be worked fair to preserve the arris *a*. Work the joints *B D* square with the bed, and scribe in the joint mould 7 *B*. Work off the top bed *c d* and splay joint *c b*, a convex templet giving the arris *B B*, and lastly, the concave surface of intrados *a b*.

The back *D D* is left rough.

Fig. 8.—To work the second stone in dome No. 8. 8 *A* is the bed mould, and 8 *B* the section, or joint mould.

Work the top bed, $b\ c\ d$—8 B, and scribe in bed mould, 8 A, to the extreme size, as $D\ D$, $B\ B$, the dotted line $A\ A$ being the horizontal arris of joint and soffit at a; the line $C\ C$ top line of splay joint c; and the line $B\ B$ the horizontal arris of joint and soffit at b 1.

Work the joints, $B\ D$ square with the top bed, and scribe in the joint mould, 8 B; at points $B\ B$, at depth b 1, work a concave draft, and draw the horizontal line of joint and arris of soffit. Next work off the splay joint $c\ b'$, also the splay joint $a\ e$, and lastly the concave surface of intrados. The back, $D\ D$. is left rough.

FIg. 10.—Shews a sketch of this stone completed.

It may be mentioned that the stones Nos. 2 and 3 (Figs. 5 and 6), previously described, are worked to one hand; for the opposite hand, the same moulds and templets will do, if reversed.

No. 5 (Fig. 2), is a plain spherical stone in the pendentive, and is worked similarly to those in the dome, as above described.

———

To construct a SPHEROIDAL DOME, with an aperture at the apex or top. The bed-joints are conical surfaces, and terminate on the extrados and intrados, in horizontal circles. The vertical joints are contained within a plane, which intersects with the axis of the dome.

Fig. 11.—Shews half-plan of the dome.

Fig. 12.—Shews section of the dome through the centre.

For the making of the moulds, and working this dome, a quarter only is necessary to be set out full-size, but in order to shew it more clearly the half is here given.

Begin by setting out on the plan (Fig. 11), the centre lines, $A\ C\ A$ and $C\ K$. With C as a centre and $C\ A$ as radius, describe the semicircle $A\ K\ A$, giving the extreme boundary of exterior surface, or extrados of dome. The thickness of the dome having been determined as $A\ B$, with C as centre and $C\ B$ as radius, describe the semicircle $B\ B$, as shewn by the dotted line, giving the extreme boundary of interior surface, or intrados of

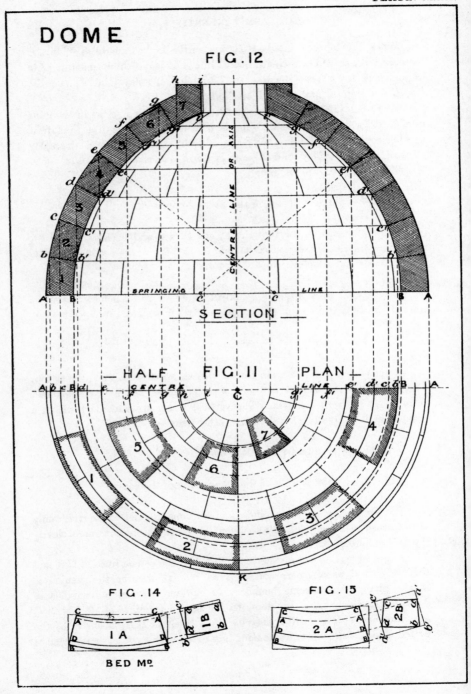

PLATE. XXXII.

DOME

FIG. 12

CENTRE LINE OR AXIS

SPRINGING LINE

SECTION

HALF FIG. II PLAN

CENTRE LINE

FIG. 14

1A 1B

BED Mᴼ

FIG. 15

2A 2B

dome. Project lines *A* and *B* to springing line, Fig. 12, and with *c c* as centres set up the section of dome, and divide the same into any number of equal parts for bed-joints as may be convenient (in this example, seven), as *b c d e f g*, and draw radiating lines for the joints from centre, *c*. Project *b c d e*, &c., on to plan (Fig. 11), and with *C* as centre describe semicircles *b c d e*, &c.; the plan of the arris of horizontal bed-joints on exterior is thus obtained. For the arris of horizontal bed-joints on interior surface, project *b c d e*, &c., on to plan, and draw the semicircles *b' c' d' e'*, &c., shewn by the dotted lines on right-hand half.

For the vertical joints each course will consist of the same number of stones (in this example, twelve), breaking joint directly over each other and diminishing in size from bottom to top course. These are set out on the plan.

The stones " hatched in " on the plan (Fig. 11), shew the projection of one voussoir in each course, as 1 2 3 4 5 6 and 7, and, being equal and similar stones, and alike in situation, one bed mould to each course only will be required.

To work the Voussoirs.

The shape of rough block required for working these stones by this method is a rectangular prism of the extreme length of the bed mould, as 1 *A* (Fig. 14), shewn by the circumscribed line, the height being that of the joint mould 1 *B*; and secondly, that of a segment of a hollow cylinder, as shewn in sketch (Fig. 17), which contains the finished block, the arrises only touching the boundaries of the cylinder.

Fig. 14.—1 *A* is the bed mould, and 1 *B* the section, or joint mould, of springer, or No. 1 stone.

Begin by working the bed, *a b*—1 *B*, and scribe in bed mould 1 *A*. Work the joints *B C* square with the bed, and scribe in joint mould 1 *B*. Work the top bed *b' c'* as a surface of operation, and scribe in the line *D D*, which gives the top line of arris of convex surface and of splay joint. With the templet *C C* at *c* work the horizontal draft, giving the arris of joint and of concave surface. Work the top, *d c*, to lines as given, and the inside concave surface *a c*; and lastly, the outside convex surface, *b d*, using templets made at *a c* and *b d* for guidance.

Fig. 15.—To work the second stone (No. 2).

2 *A* is the bed mould and 2 *B* the section, or joint mould. Work the bottom bed *a' b'* as a surface of operation, and bed *d' c'* parallel to it.

PLATE. XXXIII.

DOME

FIG. 13

— SKETCH OF DOME —

FIG. 16

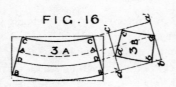

FIG. 17

FIG. 18

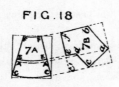

FIG. 19

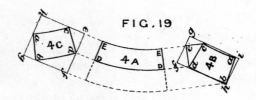

FIG. 20   FIG. 21   FIG. 22   FIG. 23

Labour need not be thrown away on these surfaces, or beds, as the arris, *a a* on one bed and *d d* on the other, is all that is required to be kept fair; the other portion may be roughly chiselled off, and at the same time kept straight. Scribe in the bed mould on both beds, as *B,C—B C*, and work the joints *B C* square with same; scribe in the joint mould, as *b a d c*, to each joint. With the templet *C C* at *c* work a horizontal draft, and draw a line parallel to *C'*, giving the arris of joint and of concave surface. With the templet *D D* scribe in line on the top bed, giving the arris of top joint and of convex surface. Work off the splay joint *d c* to the lines thus given. On the bottom bed, with templet *A A* scribe in line, giving the arris of bottom joint and of concave surface. With the templet *B B* at *b* work the horizontal draft, and draw line parallel to *b'*, giving the arris of bottom joint and of convex surface. Work off the splay joint to the lines thus given, and inside concave surface *a c,* and lastly outside convex surface *b d*, using templets made at *a c* and *b d* for guidance.

The stones in the other courses of the dome are worked in a similar manner to those last described, except the top course, or rim.

To work the Rim of Aperture in Dome, being the top, or No. 7, course.

Begin by working the top bed *c' f*, and scribe in the bed mould 7 *A*. Work the joints *C F* square with bed, and scribe in the joint mould 7 *B*. At *a* work a horizontal draft straight to *a*, and scribe in the templet *A A,* giving the arris of bottom joint and concave surface; then work the bottom joint and spherical surfaces *a b* and *c d e*.

There is some difference of opinion as to the best method of working the voussoirs in a dome, with respect to waste of material and labour. Perhaps for the first and second courses, and also the courses near the apex, no better method can be followed than the one just described, and, as before explained, in reference to vaulting, page 74. This method is simple, gives the best results, and the stones are truer in form when worked than by using a number of bevels. However, another method is here shewn, which saves much material and labour, although greater care is required in the execution.

Another Method of Working the Voussoirs.

Fig. 19.—Let 4 *A* be the bed mould of stone in fourth course of dome. (This being one of the courses in which there is much waste by the previous method of working, and is shewn by section 4 *C*, at line *e f g h*.)

For the joint mould, 4 *B*, transfer No. 4 from section (Fig. 12), as *d c b a.* Draw *e d* parallel and *e c* vertical to the base, or springing line; *f g h i* is a rectangle, circumscribing the mould and giving the size of stone required. When compared to that of 4 *C*, *e f g h*, the difference is at once seen.

Select a stone sufficiently large, so that all the surfaces and arrises are contained within it.

Fig. 20.—Begin by working a plane surface of operation, as *e d*, and apply templet 4 *A*, and scribe in as *D E, D E*. Work joints *D E* square with the bed; these require careful working, a portion of the joint being outside the line of square, as at *X X X*, but the one portion of joint having been worked, the other is obtained by means of the straight-edge. Apply joint mould to each joint, as *d c b a*, and scribe in.

Fig. 21.—Shews the next operation of working the convex spherical surface, by the guidance of a bevel, the stock of bevel being applied in the direction of a line radiating from centre *C*, as the joint lines *E D*—4 *A*.

Fig. 22.—Shews the third operation, the line *b* being drawn parallel to *d*; a bevel is used, giving the bottom splay bed, *b a*.

Fig. 23.—Shews the fourth and last operation, the angular portion, *e g d c*, being cut away and bevel used for splay joint; and the concave spherical surface is worked by the guidance of a templet made from *a c*.

It will be observed in the working of this stone that by this method the accuracy of the work depends almost entirely on the first plane surface of operation, and, should any errors occur in applying the bevels from this bed, the stone will not be of the shape and form intended.

The stones in other courses of dome may be worked in a similar manner.

PLATE. XXXIV

GROINED VAULTING

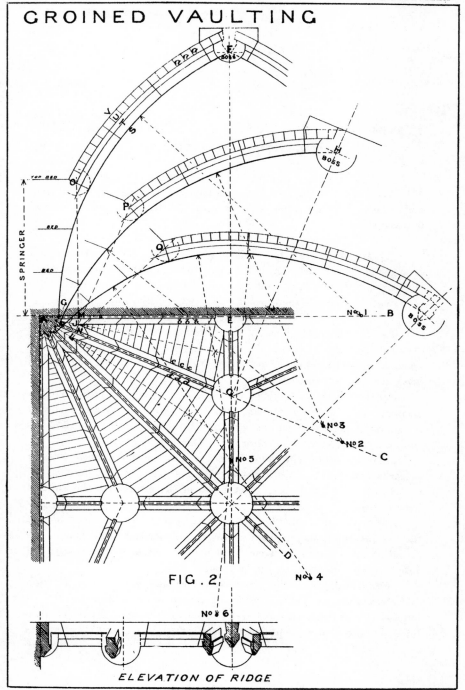

FIG. 2

ELEVATION OF RIDGE

PLATES XXXIV., XXXV., XXXVI., XXXVII.—
GROINED VAULTING.

To construct a GROINED VAULT, in four compartments, square on plan, and supported by a central shaft or column, with wall, transverse, and diagonal ribs.

Fig. 1.—Is the inverted skeleton plan of vault, shewing the general arrangement of compartments : *A A* being the wall ribs, *B B* the transverse ribs, crossing the vault at right angles to the wall, *C C* the diagonal ribs, spanning across from corners to the shaft, and *D D* the vaulting surface.

Fig. 2.—Shews the inverted plan of one compartment, or one quarter of the vault, with elevation of the wall, transverse and diagonal ribs, each being of equal height at the apex, and the ridge line of vaulting surface being also level throughout.

For the purpose of making the moulds, and the working of this vault, a small portion of the plan (one-sixteenth only), set out to full size, is all that is necessary, the remainder being a repetition ; but, in order to shew the setting out more clearly, a quarter of the plan is here given.

Begin by setting out the wall lines of vault, then the centre lines of wall ribs *A B* and *A C*, the transverse ribs *B D* and *C D*, and the diagonal ribs *A D* and *B C*, and set off on each side of the centre lines the width of their section.

Before proceeding further it is necessary to determine the position of the feet of ribs at the springing ; these generally depend on the plan of the abacus of cap, and it is also a matter of arrangement, as well as of taste and design, so that no fixed rule can be given.

In this example the ribs are arranged so that the nosings are equidistant from the point of intersection of the centre line of ribs at *A B C D*, in order that the wall ribs and transverse ribs may be of the same curvature, and also that the opening or span between the nosing of springers may be equal.

Having set out the position of the springers at A B C D on plan, the next process is to find the elevation or contour of the ribs. This is generally governed by the wall ribs, which have some opening or arch in the wall below them, regulating to some extent the form of vaulting. In some cases, perhaps, it may be preferable to begin with the transverse or diagonal rib, but this again depends on the shape of the vault.

In this example the contour of the transverse and wall ribs are similar, their span being equal, as before explained.

Begin by drawing the wall rib first. Take the centre line A B on plan, and make use of it as a base or springing line. Erect a perpendicular as a centre line at M on the plan, and on this set up the height of vault, as at E. Let point No. 1 be the centre from which the wall rib is struck, and with this as a centre, and nosing G as radius, draw the segment line S for the nose of rib on the soffit, cutting the centre line at apex E; gauge on the width of members of the rib, from the line of soffit S as H J K, and with the same centre, No. 1, draw the segment lines through these points, thus forming the wall rib. This is also the elevation of the transverse rib.

The profile of the diagonal rib is now to be obtained, and the first consideration is the shape of vault. If a horizontal section be taken through any one of the compartments, above the springers, and the vaulting, or filling in, between the ribs is rectangular in shape and parallel to the sides, the courses of stone forming the vaulting surfaces are level, and the upper edges of the diagonal ribs, upon which the filling-in rests, are portions of elliptic curves. These curves are obtained by ordinates, the curvature being subordinate to the wall rib; this is sometimes done, but as the elliptic rib entails more work both in the setting out and in the execution, the simpler method of using compound circular curves is generally adopted, and with perhaps better results constructively. The ribs are thus made geometrically regular, while the filling-in surfaces take their chance as it were, and are adjusted to the curvature of the ribs, and although twisting to some extent, yet do not offend the eye, which is guided mainly by the principal lines, and not the surfaces.

Another consideration is the separation of the ribs at one level, at the point where they become fully developed. The more equally the ribs can be grouped together at the springing, without projecting at unequal distances before each other, the better it is for their separation or clearance; the advantage of this being, that the winding in the vaulting surface is much reduced, and is free from that ploughshare-like twist, to which objection is sometimes made. The ribs are also equal in depth and of the same cross section, and the setting out and the working generally are easier. In some cases it may be impossible to do this, and the ribs are then arranged to suit the conditions of the case.

In this example the contour of the diagonal is struck from centres, and these may be varied to suit any adjustment of curvature.

The point at which the feet of ribs is struck should be on the springing line, neither above nor below, for if above the rib would be stilted, and if below an acute angle would be formed with the springing line, neither of which results is pleasing.

Let $A\,D$, the centre line of diagonal rib on plan (Fig. 2), be the base or springing line for the elevation of rib; produce the centre line $C\,B$, which is perpendicular to $A\,D$, as the centre line of elevation, and on this set up, from the base line to the apex of the soffit of rib, the height $N\,L$, equal to the height $M\,E$ on the elevation of the wall rib. Next in the elevation of wall rib, find the point of clearance, or where the rib separates from the springer, and the full section of rib is obtained; this will be the point in the upper edge of the rib vertically over the point where the sides of the rib intersect at P on plan. At P erect a perpendicular to the springing line $A\,B$, cutting the upper edge of rib at O in elevation, which is the point of separation, or where the wall rib is fully developed, and clears the springer. Through the same point P, erect a perpendicular to the springing line $A\,D$ on the diagonal, and set off the height $F\,Q$, equal to the height at wall rib of $G\,O$; the diagonal rib thus clears the springer at point Q, the back edge of the rib at vaulting surface.

Two points are already given in the curve of the diagonal rib, namely at F, the springing, and at L, the apex, but a third is required. Now at point Q describe an arc with radius equal to the depth of the rib as at O, and it will be at once evident that the arc furnishes a point through which the curve of rib must be drawn. Commence on the springing line $A\,D$, and find a centre by which the curve may be drawn from F, to touch the arc whose centre is Q, but as this throws the curve too high, and would make a cripple, find a centre, No. 2, that takes the curve still higher, that is to R as shewn by the dotted line. Now find a centre as No. 3, and draw curve to R from the apex L. An intermediate radius is now required, by which a curve may be drawn touching the arc whose centre is Q, and intersecting the other curves Nos. 2 and 3. This is found at No. 4, and the curvature of the diagonal rib thus obtained is easy and graceful, retaining also the pointed form. Gauge on the width of members of the rib from the line of soffit, and with their respective radii draw curves forming the elevation of the diagonal rib.

PLATE. XXXV

GROINED VAULTING

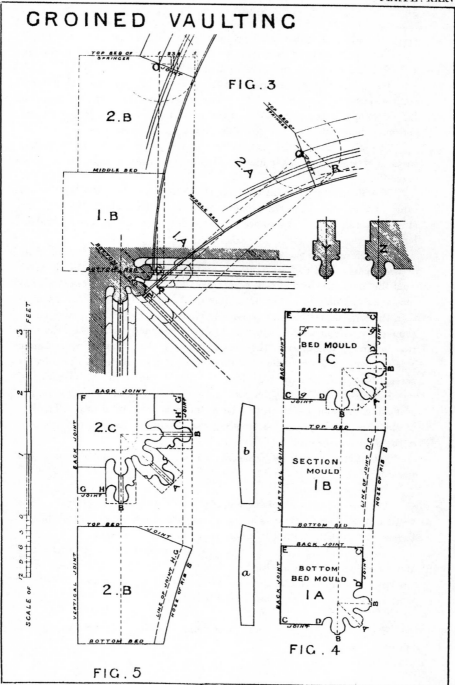

FIG. 3

FIG. 4

FIG. 5

The radii and centres are best found by repeated trials.

The next thing to be done is to arrange the joints of the springers and ribs, and the filling-in to the vaulted surfaces.

The joints of the springers are usually worked in horizontal or level courses, except a portion of the top bed, where the ribs separate and are fully developed; this portion is inclined or splayed from the level bed, and abutment joints are thus formed which radiate to their centres.

The joints for the ribs may be drawn to any convenient length to suit the size of stones, and they must radiate to the centres from which that part of the rib is struck.

The diagonal ribs which intersect at the apex and form the key are the same in curvature, and will properly mitre into each other; the arms or stumps at each side of the intersection are drawn at will to any convenient length.

The filling-in to the vaulted surfaces is in narrow bands of stone, four or five inches wide, and with beds slightly radiating. These bands start from the point where the ribs separate at the top of springers, and are continued in parallel courses until they meet obliquely at the apex, taking then the form of key blocks; these key blocks are rack shaped, and derive support from the bands which abut against them, and also rest on the wall ribs and mitre junctions in the centre of the vault. The filling-in bands being narrow on the face the twist to each stone is so small as to be scarcely perceptible; moulds may be made to these if desired from the elevation of wall and diagonal ribs, but the twist on the stones is usually worked on the scaffold at the time of fixing, this being the most economical way. The key blocks also are simple in construction, the making of moulds and working of the stones presenting no difficulty.

Attention may now be directed to the setting out in detail and to the working of the various stones.

Fig. 3.—Shews the setting out of the springers to a larger scale. The section moulds for diagonal and transverse ribs are given at Y, and that of the wall rib, which is slightly different on the wall side, at Z.

The centre lines having been drawn, the section moulds of ribs Y and Z are applied until the position of the ribs is arranged equi-distant from the point of intersection of the centre lines, as before explained.

The notation is the same as that of Fig. 2.

Fig. 4.—Shews the bed and joint moulds of No. 1, or bottom stone in springer.

PLATE. XXXVI.

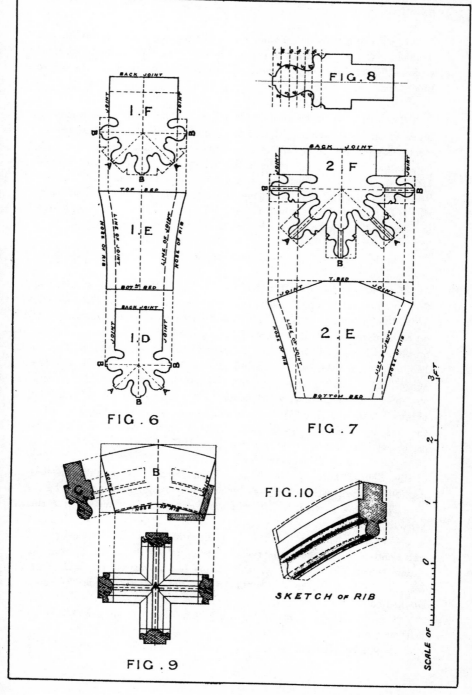

FIG. 8

FIG. 6

FIG. 7

FIG. 10

SKETCH OF RIB

FIG. 9

SCALE OF

1 *A* is the bottom bed mould, 1 *C* is the top bed mould or middle bed (this also will be the bottom bed mould of No. 2, or upper stone in springer at dotted line *g f g*), and 1 *B* is the section mould taken through the centre line of wall rib.

Commence by working the back joints *E C* and *E C'* (which may be taken as surfaces of operation), and scribe on the section mould 1 *B* on each joint. Work the bottom and top beds square from back joint, these being parallel to each other, and scribe in the bed moulds 1 *A* on bottom bed and 1 *C* on the top bed. Work the two concave joints *C D* and *C' D'*, guided by a convex templet, and the nosing of rib from *A* to *A* and the nosing of ribs *B* to *B*, guided by the convex templets *a* and *b*. The moulding is now to be worked, using small reverses and templets for guidance.

Fig. 5.—Shews the bed and joint mould of No. 2 or upper stone of the springer.

1 *C* (Fig. 4) is the bottom bed mould, 2 *C* is the top bed mould, and 2 *B* is the section mould taken through the centre line of the wall rib. Work the back joints *F G* and *F G'*, and scribe on the section mould 2 *B* on each joint. Work off the bottom bed square from the back joint, scribing on the bed mould 1 *C* (Fig. 4) to the dotted line *f g*; next work off the top bed square from the back joint and parallel to the bottom bed, and the splay joint seating for the wall rib, as given by section mould 2 *B*, also the splay joint for the seating of diagonal rib. The bevel for this may be obtained from 2 *A* (Fig. 3) or the nose line may be squared down from the top bed and the depth gauged on. On the centre lines of the top bed scribe on the section of rib moulds *Y* and *Z*. Work the two concave joints *G H* and *G' H'*, also the nosing of rib from *A* to *A* and the nosing of ribs from *B* to *B*, guided by convex templets. The moulding is now carefully worked, using small reverses and templets for guidance.

The springers when worked will truly mitre from the springing to the separation of ribs.

Care must be taken that the centre lines of the ribs are vertically over one another, or in the same vertical plane, as shewn in Fig. 5—2 *C*, in which the mould No. 1 *C* for the bottom bed is marked on, and again in Fig. 7—2 *F*, where the mould 1 *F*, for the bottom bed, is also marked on.

The moulds should always be made this way with the sections vertically over one another.

It will be observed in the bed mould 2 *C* (Fig. 5) that although the moulding to ribs is given it is only approximate, and cannot be worked to accurately, because it is here foreshortened, and consequently a little distorted. This may be seen by reference to Fig. 3, the plane at 1, 2, 3, 4, 5 being that to which the mouldings are projected from the splay joint. The position of nosing, however, is correctly given, starting square down at the depth of the splay joint from the horizontal bed. .

The section of the rib moulding at the middle bed, or at any horizontal line of the springer, may be obtained by projection. Divide the square section of the rib into any number of parts as in Fig. 8 at 1 2 3 4 5 6. Set off these points on the elevation of the rib, and from the centre draw the segmental lines through, cutting the horizontal line or bed; transfer these points of intersection to the centre line of the rib on plan, and draw lines through square from the centre line, and make them equal to 1 1—2 2—3 3, &c., of square section, and draw the curves through these points, giving the true section at horizontal level.

Fig. 6.—Shews the bed and joint moulds of springers of No. 1 or bottom stone at B and C on the plan (Fig. 2).

1 D is the bottom bed mould, 1 F is the top bed mould, and 1 E is the section mould taken through the centre line of wall rib B B.

Fig. 7.—Shews the bed and joint moulds of No. 2 or upper stone of springers at B and C on the plan (Fig. 2).

1 F (Fig. 6) is the bottom bed mould, 2 F is the top bed mould, and 2 E is the section mould taken through the centre line of wall rib B B.

The moulds for the central springer at D on the shaft are identical with the last-named (Fig. 6 and Fig. 7). The centre line at B B being half of the mould, this half scribed on the stone and then reversed for the other half, gives a completed whole.

These last-named springers are worked precisely as those already described, the same templets as before being used for the nosing of ribs and concave joints.

Fig. 9.—Shews the bed and section mould of the key-stone at the intersection of the diagonal ribs. A is the bed mould, B is the section mould, taken vertically through the centre, and C is the section mould of the rib.

Work a plane bed as a surface of operation, and scribe in the bed mould *A* on the soffit. Work off the splay joints to bevel, and scribe in the section mould of rib *C* on each joint; work out the square checks on each side of ribs, and cut the nosings to a concave shape, guided by convex templets. Now run the mouldings in on each stump to their intersection, forming mitres, cut off the back if required, and take out the rebate for vaulting surfaces.

Fig. 10.—Shews a sketch of the rib.

The working of this requires but little description, it being treated as a simple arch stone. A plane surface is first formed; on this the face mould is scribed, and the joints which radiate from the curve of the soffit are then squared through, and the section mould of rib is scribed in on each joint. The stone is next worked to a parallel thickness, the rebate for vaulting surface being taken out and the moulding run through, guided by convex templets and reverses.

Fig. 11.—Shews a sketch of part of the vault.

PLATE. XXXVII.

GROINED VAULTING

FIG. II

SKETCH OF PART OF VAULT

FIG. I

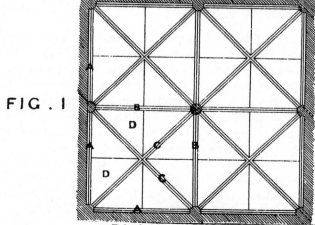

PLAN OF VAULT

Plates XXXVIII., XXXIX., XL., XLI.—GROINED VAULTING.

(*Continued.*)

To construct a Groined Vault, square on plan, with wall, diagonal, intermediate and ridge ribs.

This vault is somewhat different to the one previously shewn on pages 89 and 90, in having intermediate ribs, ridge ribs, and bosses.

Ornamental bosses are introduced into these vaults, as it is not possible to nicely mitre the mouldings of the ribs, at the intersection of the apex or ridge, on account of the differing inclinations of the ribs. The mouldings, therefore, die into the bosses, and the difficulty is got over. The bosses also give strength and richness to the vault.

Fig. 1.—Is the inverted plan of vault, shewing the general arrangement of ribs, *A A* being the wall ribs, *B B* the diagonal ribs, *C C* the intermediate ribs, *D D* the ridge ribs, and *E* the vaulting surface, or filling in, and *F* the bosses.

Fig. 2.—Shews the inverted plan, of one quarter of the vault, with elevation of the wall, diagonal, intermediate, and ridge ribs, each being of equal height at the apex, and the ridge ribs being also level throughout.

For the purpose of making the moulds and working the vault, only one quarter is necessary to be set out, the remainder being a repetition. Begin as previously described on page 89 by setting out the wall lines of vault, then the centre lines of wall, ridge, intermediate, and diagonal ribs, and draw circles for bosses, at the intersection of ribs.

Determine the position of the feet of ribs, at the springing line, as shewn at Fig. 3. The noses of these ribs are arranged so as to touch a segmental line (the abacus of cap upon which the springer rests being segmental). Gauge off on each side of the centre lines the width of ridge, intermediate, diagonal, and wall ribs; the first three are equal, but the

PLATE. XXXIV.

GROINED VAULTING

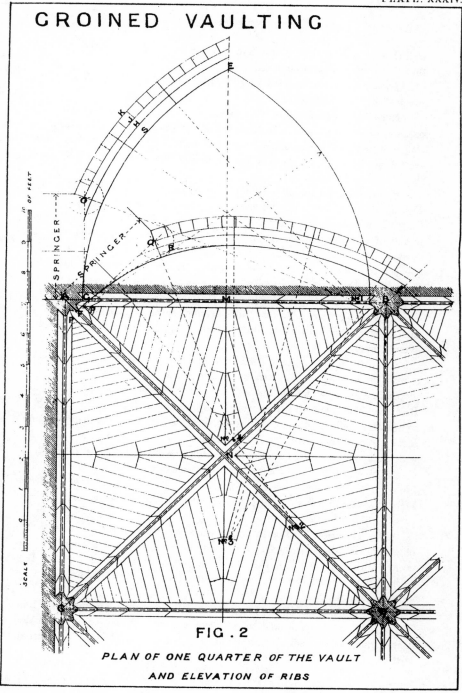

FIG . 2

PLAN OF ONE QUARTER OF THE VAULT
AND ELEVATION OF RIBS

wall ribs are only a little more than half the width of the others, in order that the nosings should be of one size.

To complete the portion of the plan, the filling in, to the vaulted surface, must now be set out.

Narrow bands of stone, or chalk, of various widths, but generally parallel, are mostly used. In the spandrel pieces on the plan, between the wall and intermediate ribs, and intermediate and diagonal ribs, the joints are set out at right angles to a line bisecting the angle formed by these ribs.

Space out these bands, on the rebate line of wall rib, on the elevation Fig. 2, as at *a a a*, and project on to the side of the wall rib on plan, as at *b b b*; draw the joints at right angles to the line of bisection, which produce to side of the intermediate rib as *c c c*. Square the joints across this rib as shewn at *d d d*; the points thus obtained give the position of the bands, between the intermediate and the diagonal rib, which are drawn similarly to the preceding.

The next process is to find the elevation, or contour of ribs, which in the present example is governed by the wall rib, and this regulates to some extent the form of vaulting.

Begin by drawing the wall rib, taking the centre line *A B* on plan as a base or springing line, then at *E*, the centre of side of vault, erect a perpendicular as a centre line, and set up the height of vault as at *F*. Point No. 1 is the centre from which the wall rib is struck, with this point as a centre, and the distance to nosing *G* as radius, draw the segment line *S* for the nose of rib on the soffit, cutting the centre line at the apex *F*, which may be also called a datum line, this line being the height to which all the ribs are drawn. Next gauge on the width of the members of rib, from the line of soffit *S*, as *T U V*, and with the same centre No. 1 draw segmental lines through these points, thus completing the wall rib.

The elevation of the intermediate and diagonal ribs is now to be obtained, and the first consideration is the separation of the ribs at one level. This separation of the ribs is of primary importance both in the working and the setting out, and has been fully explained in the previous section, page 91.

For the elevation of the intermediate rib, commence on the centre line of rib *A C* on the plan, and at *G* erect a perpendicular to *A C* as the centre line; on this set up the height *G H*, equal to *E F*, on the elevation of the wall rib.

PLATE. XXXIX.

FIG . 1

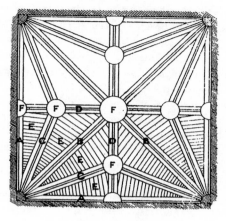

SCALE ⊢───┴──┴──┴──┴──┴──┘ OF FEET

FIG . 8

Next find the point in the elevation of the wall rib, where the rib clears itself and separates from the springer. At J erect a perpendicular to the springing line A B, cutting the upper edge of the rib at O, in elevation, which is the point of separation of the rib, or where it is fully developed, and clears the springer. Through the same point J erect a perpendicular to the springing line A C on the intermediate rib, and set off the height N P, equal to the height of wall rib at M O. The intermediate rib thus clears the springer at point P, the back edge of rib at vaulting surface. Two points are already given in the curve of the intermediate rib, namely, at R the springing, and at H the apex, but a third is required. Now at point P describe an arc, with radius equal to the depth of the rib as at O, containing a point through which the curve of rib must be drawn. Commence on the springing line A C, and find by trial a centre, and draw the curve from R to touch or approach the arc, whose centre is P. Find a centre No. 2, and draw the curve from R towards the arc, and with centre No. 3 continue the curve to apex H. From the line of soffit gauge the width of members of rib, and with centres Nos. 2 and 3 draw the curves, forming the elevation of the intermediate rib. Care must be taken that the curves are regular, and that cripples are avoided.

The elevation of the diagonal rib is to be next obtained, and the method adopted is similar to the foregoing, or as in the preceding example, page 92. Centres are found by trial, as at Nos. 4, 5, and 6, and the curves drawn from them.

The next thing to be done is to arrange the joints of the springers, and the ribs, and these may be drawn to any convenient size. The joints of the ribs, above the springers, radiate to their respective centres, and the joints of the springers will have horizontal beds.

The moulds and templets for the springers are made, and the stones worked similarly to those already described in preceding example, pages 94, 96, 97.

The ridge ribs and the bosses have now to be described, for the purpose of making the moulds, and working of the stones.

Fig. 4.—Is the bed mould and sections of the central boss stone, A being the bed mould, B the section mould, through the centre of the boss, and curved ribs, and C is part section mould, through the centre of boss,

PLATE. XL.

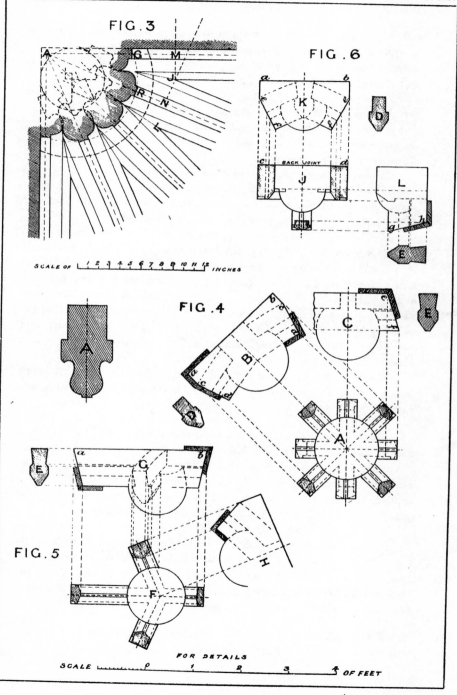

FIG. 3

FIG. 6

SCALE OF |1 2 3 4 5 6 7 8 9 10 11 12| INCHES

FIG. 4

FIG. 5

FOR DETAILS

SCALE |........0   1   2   3   4| OF FEET

and ridge ribs. It will be seen that neither of these last two moulds can be applied direct on the stone, but are used to obtain the bevels of the joints, curvature and position of the ribs, and contour for the carving, as well as to shew the true form at those sections,

The stumps, or arms, in this example are perhaps longer than they need be, but are here emphasised to shew more clearly the working. The four joints of the diagonal ribs radiate to their centres, and form a key, the other four joints are arranged so as to form skew backs, upon which the ridge stones are supported.

There are several ways of working these boss stones, and the one now to be described is similar to that adopted by the old Gothic masons, which has also simplicity to recommend it. There must necessarily be waste of stone as well as labour, whatever method is chosen.

First form a plane surface of operation, as *a b* on the section *B*, so that when fixed, this bed is horizontal, and on this scribe in the bed mould *A*. Work off the splay joints *e f* to receive ridge, the bevel being obtained from the section *C*, and the radiating joints *c d*, for the diagonal ribs, getting the bevel for these from section *B*, scribe in the section mould of rib *E*, to splay joint for the ridge, and the section mould of rib *D*, to the radiating joint for the diagonal ribs. Now work the stumps and mouldings in against the boss, using templets made from section moulds *B* and *C* for guidance.

The boss may be shaped out and carved before fixing, or left rough from the point, and carved after fixing, the latter method being generally adopted.

Fig. 5.—Is the bed mould and sections of intermediate boss stone, and part of the ridge, *F* being the bed mould, *G* the section mould, through the centre of the boss and ridge rib, and *H* part section mould through the boss and intermediate ribs. Neither of these last two moulds can be applied, but are used for the purpose of obtaining bevels, curvature, and position of ribs, &c., as in the case of central boss stone (Fig. 4.)

First form a plane surface of operation, which will be horizontal, as *a b*, on the section *G*, and on this scribe in the bed mould *F*, then rough the stone out to shape and work off the joints, the bevels being obtained from the section moulds *G* and *H*, scribe in the section moulds *E*, for the ridge rib, and *D* for the intermediate ribs. Next work the ribs in against boss, and complete the mouldings; the boss may be treated as in Fig. 4.

Fig. 6.—Shews the bed mould, and also sections of key to ridge and wall ribs, *J* being the bed mould, *K* and *L* the section moulds.

First form a plane surface of operation, which is horizontal as *a b* on the section *K*, and on this scribe in the bed mould *J*, work off the vertical back joint *c d*, and scribe in the section mould *K*, and work the splay joints *e f* through for wall ribs. Next work the splay joint *g h*, by aid of bevel taken from the section *L*, and scribe in the section mould of ribs, cut ribs in against boss, and complete the mouldings. The boss may be treated as in Fig. 4.

In Fig. 3, at section *A*, the mouldings to ribs are shewn, but in the other figures these mouldings are represented by a chamfer, on account of the smallness of the scale to which they are drawn.

On the plan of the springing (Fig. 3), the letters are identical with those at the springing on the smaller scale (Fig. 2), in order that the reference to them may be more clear.

Fig. 7.—Shews a sketch of part of the vault.

Fig. 8.—The extent to which vaulting of a complicated nature may be carried out is shewn in the plan here given of part of the vaulting at the Members' private entrance, House of Commons.

The student may be reminded that the examples here given of groined vaulting deal only with a small portion of this intricate subject, but it is hoped that the general principles have been sufficiently illustrated, so as to enable him to deal with other cases as they come before him.

PLATE. XLI

GROINED VAULTING

FIG. 7

SKETCH OF PART OF VAULT

PLATES XLII., XLIII., XLIV., XLV., XLVI.— TRACERY WINDOWS.

TRACERY WINDOWS are of the most extensive variety, both in design and form, and require no little consideration and study on the part of the student. The correct carrying out of the designs for such works affords valuable evidence of the mason's skill.

Without going into the principles governing the composition and design of tracery, it may be remarked that, with few exceptions, geometrical tracery is based upon the combination of the equilateral triangle with the polygon and circle; and the examples here given will mostly illustrate this particular style.

In setting out tracery windows generally, commence by drawing the vertical centre line of window, then the springing line at right angles to the same, and set off the span, or opening, and draw segment line of the arch. Divide the span for small openings, and draw in the mullions. This may also be obtained from the plan if first drawn. Now draw in the construction lines for centres of tracery to the required design, care being taken that the curves must properly intersect with each other, or be drawn tangental, as the case may be. The mouldings which form the mullion, on taking a curved shape in the tracery, are termed monials.

Gauge on from the centre lines of tracery last drawn the width of monial, giving the lines of nosings, fillets, splays, &c., and complete the window by drawing the foliations, eyes, and cusps.

The joints of all tracery windows should be drawn in to radiating lines from the centres, by which the principal curves of monials are drawn; this is not always possible, but the rule should be borne in mind.

For the purpose of making the moulds, one half the window only is necessary to be set out.

Fig. 1.—Shews the constructional lines of completed window (Fig. 2). The equilateral triangle *A B C*, divided into four similar figures *d d d*,

PLATE. XLII.

TRACERY WINDOWS

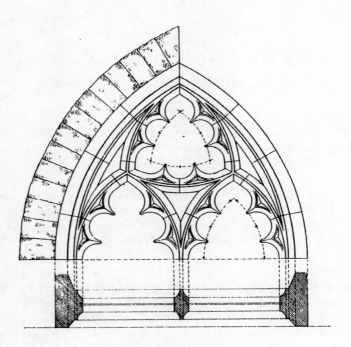

FIG . 2

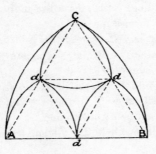

FIG . I

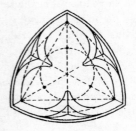

FIG . 3

PLATE. XLIII.

TRACERY WINDOWS

FIG . 5

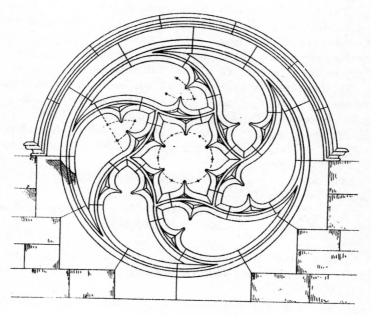

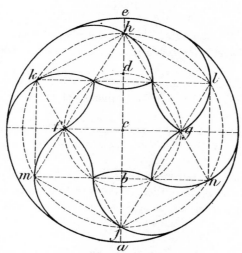

FIG . 4

gives the centres for the tracery. This is again exemplified in Fig. 3, which shews the trefoil, the centres of which are evident, and need no description.

Fig. 4.—Shews the constructional lines of circular window (Fig. 5).

To construct the figure, divide the diameter into four equal parts, as at *b c d e*, and with *c* as centre and *b* or *d* as radius, describe a circle, and inscribe a regular hexagon, intersecting with the opposite diameter at *f g*. The points of intersection will give one half of the centres of tracery.

On the diameter at *f g*, as a common base, construct the two equilateral triangles *f g h* and *f g j*, and with *c* as centre, and *h* or *j* the apex, as radius, describe a circle, and inscribe the hexagon *h j k l m n*, or produce the equilateral triangles, cutting the circles in these points. These give the other half of the centres, for completing the main lines of tracery.

Fig. 5.—Is the completed window, with foliations, eyes, and cusps, and label moulding.

It may be observed, that four face moulds, with a slight modification in two of them, will work all the tracery in this window.

Fig. 6.—Shews the elevation and part plan of window, the right-hand half in elevation, shewing constructional lines, and the left hand the completed half of window.

This will be understood without further instruction than is afforded by the illustration.

Fig. 7.—Shews the elevation and part plan of window, the right-hand half in elevation shewing constructional lines, and the left-hand the completed half of window.

The geometrical constructive lines are not so marked or apparent in this window, yet it has a purely geometrical expression, the trefoil and circle predominating.

This example has been chosen to illustrate the working of one of the stones, which is typical of the working of each of the others.

Fig. 8.—Shews face mould of the springer *A*, transferred from elevation (Fig. 7). *B B* are section moulds of main monials, *C* is section mould of mullion, or bottom bed, of springer, and *D* is section mould of small monial ; this applies to the two branch joints.

To work the springer, commence by working a plane, as a surface of

PLATE. XLV.

TRACERY WINDOWS

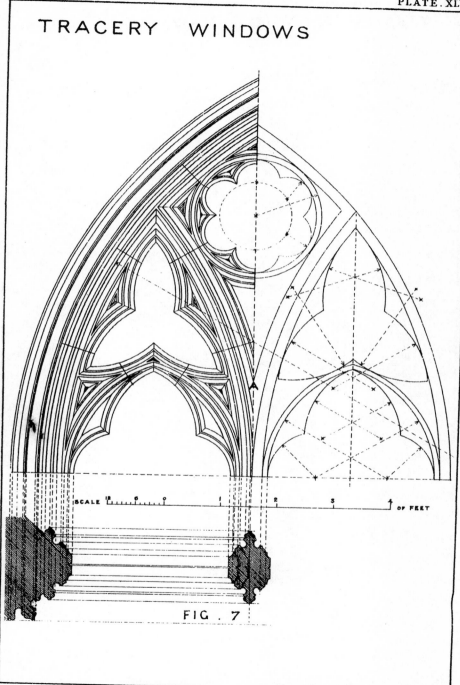

SCALE 12 6 0 1 2 3 4 OF FEET

FIG . 7

PLATE. XLIV.

TRACERY WINDOWS

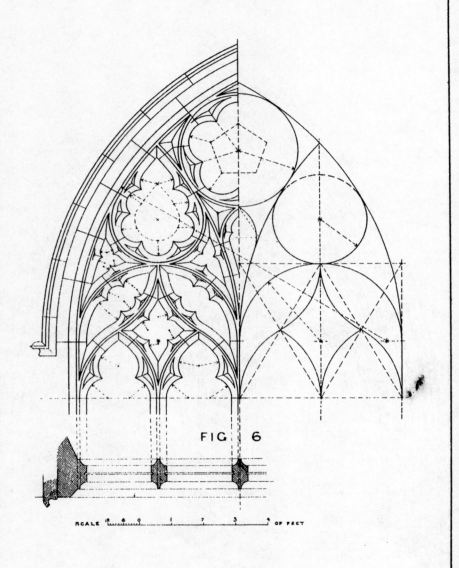

FIG 6

SCALE ᵁ⁶ ⁶ ⁰ 1 2 3 4 OF FEET

operation, and on this scribe in the face mould *A*, marking-in the nosings *a a b* by the aid of a templet, the nosings being the only portion of the plane not cut away. Next point the stone roughly to shape of the face mould, and then take it to a parallel thickness, equal to the thickness of the section mould *B* or *C*. Now work the joints through square from the face, and scribe in joint moulds *B D* and *C* on their respective joints. Then work through the nosing *a a* and *b*, and boutel mouldings, and fillets, and sink down the whole of the remainder of face to lower nosing *c c c*, scribe in on each side of nosing the skeleton face mould (Fig. 9), and work the soffits through to shape. Sinkings are now made for the several mouldings, the eyes of cusps are pierced, and the stone finished to its correct shape, templets and reverses being used in guidance.

Fig. 9.—The using of the skeleton mould, here illustrated, saves the working through of the soffits, from the outside, or first surface of operation.

The section moulds for monials, in several cases, will require a little widening out, as at *D*, and these may be projected from the face mould. The reason for this is, that the joints are not always on a true sectional line.

Fig. 10.—Shews sketches of various examples of cusps, which require no explanation.

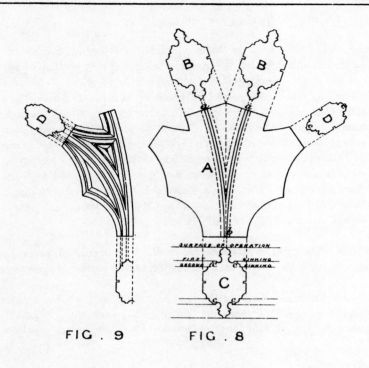

FIG . 9   FIG . 8

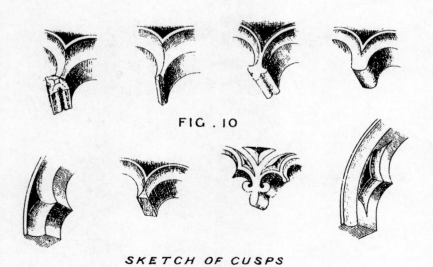

FIG . 10

SKETCH OF CUSPS

PLATES XLVII., XLVIII., XLIX., L.—GOTHIC MOULDINGS.

The profiles of mouldings here given are indications of the various styles or periods, and are of great interest to the student of Masonry, and also because they attest the working skill of the mason.

The characteristics generally of each period and the dates are briefly as follows :—

Norman, 1066 to 1189.

The mouldings consist chiefly of chamfers, round, and quarter round members, with shallow hollows, the edge roll or bead being the principal member. These are frequently entirely covered with ornament, such as the chevron or zigzag, the billet, the lozenge, the double cone, the star, the pellet, and others, producing great richness of effect.

Early English, 1189 to 1300.

In this period the mouldings are bold and deeply undercut, and generally arranged on rectangular planes; they are composed chiefly of the bowtell and keel members, with a combination of fillets and deep hollows of irregular curves, resulting in a beautiful effect of light and shade. The curves of these mouldings are easy and graceful, and are usually drawn by hand, the compasses being little used.

The principal ornament of these mouldings is the dog-tooth, which is greatly varied, and belongs exclusively to this style.

Decorated, 1300 to 1377.

The mouldings in this style are bold and well-proportioned, and arranged on rectangular as well as diagonal planes. The rounds and hollows are not so deeply cut as in the preceding style, the hollows being segments of circles, the deeper hollows being confined to the inner angles; the roll moulding, the quarter round, and wave moulding are also very much used in combination of the groups.

The ornament is chiefly the ball flower, of which there are several varieties, and the four-leaved or diaper flower; these are nearly as characteristic of the Decorated style as the tooth ornament is of the Early English.

Perpendicular, 1377 to 1547.

This style is characterized by mouldings which have large and shallow members, and generally a large hollow in the centre of each group, and arranged on diagonal planes. Another feature of this style is the constant use of beads of three-quarters of a circle and also flat wave mouldings; to this may be added the absence of fine detail.

The common ornaments are the Tudor flower, rose, and fleur-de-lys cresting, an example of the last-named being given on Plate 50.

[*To face Plate XLVII.*

GOTHIC MOULDINGS.

PROFILES OF GOTHIC MOULDINGS.

Norman Period, 1066 *to* 1189.

1 to 5. Cushion caps of various forms, principally from Peterborough Cathedral.

6 to 14. Bases, various.

15. Base from nave, Worksop Priory.

16. Arch mould from transept, Peterborough.

17. Arch and label mould from nave, Tutbury.

18.   ,,   ,,   ,,   Southwell.

19.   ,, mould from transept, Peterborough.

20.   ,, and label from mould nave, Worksop Priory.

21.   ,,   ,,   ,,   Wenlock Priory.

22.   ,,   ,,   ,,   transept, Peterborough.

23.   ,,   ,, with various enrichments.

24 to 29. Strings, various.

30. The sunk star ornament.

31.   ,, billet   ,,

32.   ,, square billet ,,

33.   ,, lozenge   ,,

34.   ,, double cone ,,

35.   ,, chevron or zigzag.

36.   ,, beakhead.

1A, 2A. Ornament in caps, Worksop Priory.

NORMAN PERIOD — 1066 TO 1189.

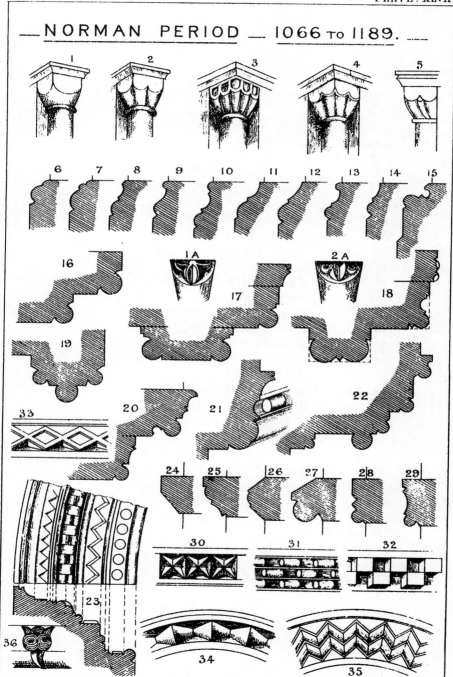

[To face Plate XLVIII.

GOTHIC MOULDINGS.

Early English Period, **1189 to 1300.**

1, 2, 8. Caps from Westminster Abbey, Triforium.

4 and 6.   „   „   Bolton Abbey.

5, 7, 8.   „   „   various.

9.   „   „   from Carlisle Cathedral.

10. Base from Carlisle Cathedral.

11.   „   Ely   „

12.   „   Peterborough Cathedral.

18.   „   Cowling, Kent.

14.   „   Lincoln Cathedral.

15 to 19. Bases, various.

20. Base from Warmington, N. Hants.

21.   „   Durham Cathedral.

22.   „   Lincoln   „   Arcade.

28.   „   Bolton Abbey.

24, 25. Arch and label moulds, Warmington, N. Hants.

26.   „   „   Carlisle Cathedral.

27. Jamb mould.

28. Arch and label moulds, Warmington, Doorway.

29. Arch mould, Lincoln Cathedral, Arcade.

30.   „   Langham Church, S. Transept.

81.   „   Beaulieu, Hants.

82.   „

88, 84, 85. Bowtell mouldings.

86, 87. Keel mouldings.

88 to 44. String mouldings, various.

45, 46. Rib mouldings.

47, 48. Mullion.

49. Scroll moulding.

50. Roll and triple fillet.

51. Dog-tooth ornament.

52. Crocket   „

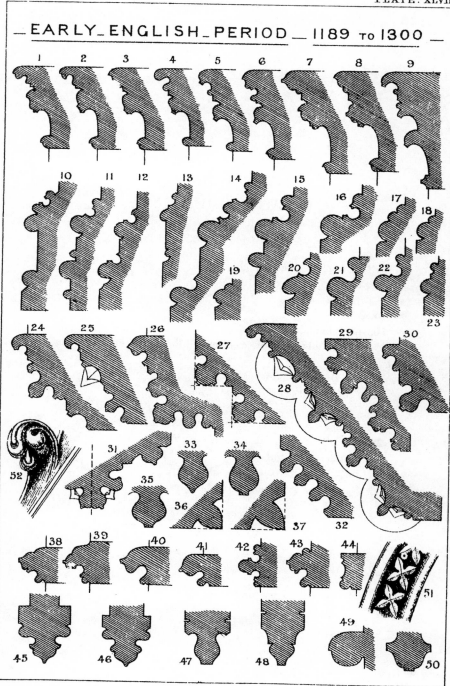

PLATE. XLVIII.

_EARLY_ENGLISH_PERIOD_ 1189 to 1300 _

GOTHIC MOULDINGS.

Decorated Period, 1300 *to* 1377.

1. Cap from Irthlingborough.

2 to 8. Caps, various.

9 to 14. Bases, various.

15. Mullion.

16. Jamb mould.

17. Arch mould with ornament of ball flower and four-leaved or diaper flower.

18, 19, 20. Arch and label moulds.

21. Arch mould from Lichfield, Choir.

22.　　,,　　,,　　,, Stafford, Nave.

23. Jamb　　,,　　,, Holbeach Church, Lincolnshire.

24 to 30. String and label moulds, various.

31. Triple filleted roll.

32 to 35. Varieties of wave mouldings.

36. Ball-flower ornament, three varieties.

PLATE. XLIX.

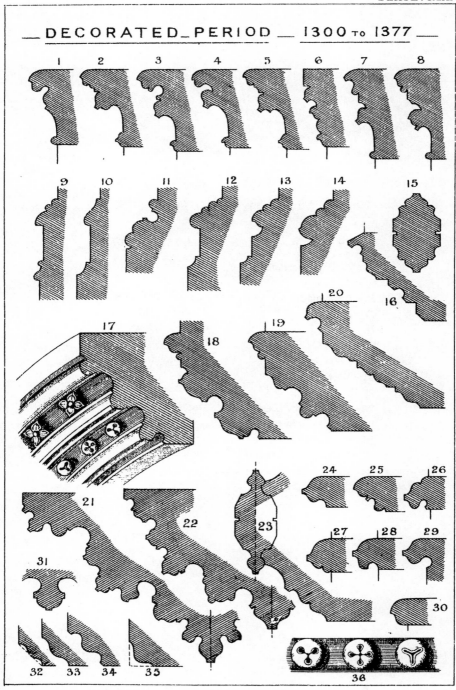

DECORATED _ PERIOD _ 1300 to 1377 _

GOTHIC MOULDINGS.

Perpendicular Period, 1877 *to* 1547.

1 to 7. Caps, various.

8 to 15. Bases, ,,

16. Arch mould and label from Chester Cathedral.

17.   ,,   ,,   Newark, Nave.

18.   ,,   ,,

19. Jamb mould.

20. Pier   ,,   from St. Stephen's Cloisters, Westminster.

21. Wave moulding.

22.   ,,   ,,

23. Mullion, St. Stephen's Cloisters.

24. Rib moulding   ,,   ,,

25. Buttress moulding.

26 to 33. Strings and labels, various.

34. Sill mould, Christchurch.

35. Cresting ornament.

PLATE. L.

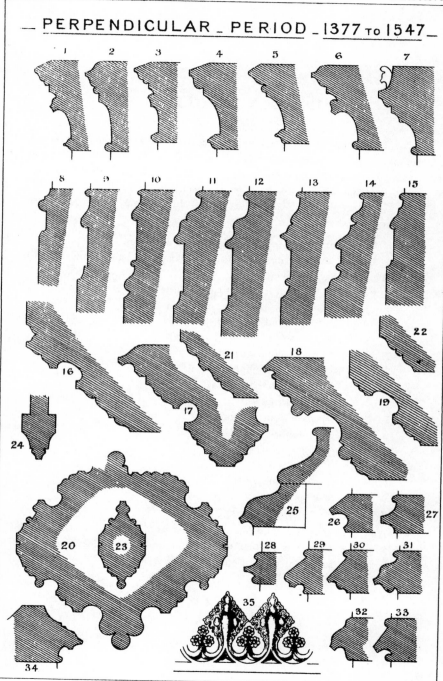

PERPENDICULAR – PERIOD – 1377 TO 1547 –

GRECIAN MOULDINGS.

The profiles of these mouldings are composed of lines of varying curvature, and mostly correspond to conic sections, embracing the hyperbola, parabola, and ellipse. It is considered, however, that they were drawn by hand, and not obtained by any mechanical method.

The examples here shown are taken chiefly from the works of Sir William Chambers and Inwood.

1. Section of the Doric cornice from the Parthenon.
2. Plan of external angle of ditto, looking up, showing the mutules and honeysuckle enrichment.
3. Section of Ionic cornice from the Erectheium.
4.   ,,   ,,   ,,   ,,
5. Doric cap from Samothrace (Hyperbola).
6.   ,,   from the Theseum (Parabola).
7.   ,,   from Selinus (Ellipse).
8. Ionic base from the Temple on the Ilyssus.
9.   ,,   from Minerva Polias.
10.   ,,   from Prienne.
11. Corinthian base from Monument of Lysicrates.
12. Capital of Antæ from Erectheium.
13.   ,,   ,,
14.   ,,   ,,
15. Egg and tongue enrichment.
16. Annulets or neckings to Doric caps.

Note.—It may be here observed that the columns of the Greek Doric have no base, but are planted direct on the square step which is a feature of this particular style of building.

PLATE. LI.

GRECIAN_MOULDINGS

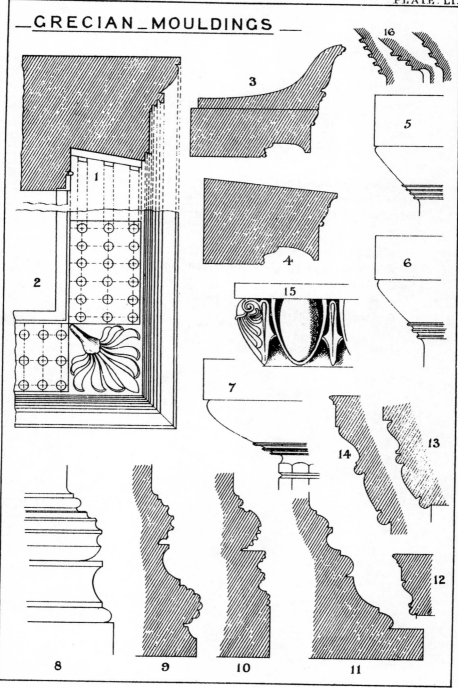

ROMAN MOULDINGS.

These mouldings are all derived from Greek originals, but without their refinement of outline, and in artistic beauty are far below their predecessors. The profiles are in most cases composed of segments of circles.

1. Elevation of Doric cornice.
2. Plan of external angle of ditto, looking up, showing the modillions.
3. Elevation of Doric cap.
4. Section of capping to Doric pedestal.
5. Section of Architrave.
6. ,, ,,
7. Section of pedestal capping.
8. ,, ,,
9. Section of Tuscan base.
10. ,, Doric base.
11. ,, Corinthian base.
12. ,, Composite base.
13. ,, pedestal plinth.
14. ,, ,,
15. Baluster (enriched).
16. ,,
17. ,,

PLATE. LII.

ROMAN MOULDINGS

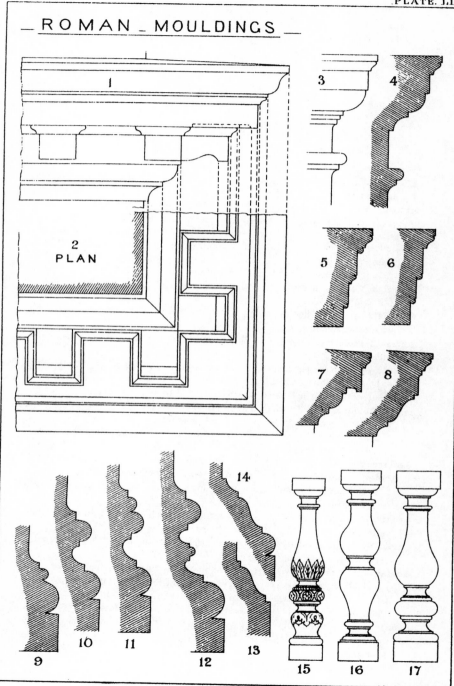

1

2
PLAN

3 4

5 6

7 8

9 10 11 12 13 14

15 16 17

GLOSSARY OF TERMS.

Abacus.—The tablet or the upper member of the capital of a column ; varying in the several orders and styles.

Abutment.—The solid part of a pier which receives the thrust or lateral pressure of the arch, and from which the arch immediately springs.

Alabaster.—A white translucent species of gypsum or sulphate of lime, composed of crystalline grains in a compact mass. It is capable of being worked to a high degree of finish, and taking a fine polish.

It is much used for interior decorations, monuments, &c.

Annular Vault.—A vault springing from two walls, each circular on plan.— *See* Plate XXVII.

Annulet.—A small fillet encircling a column, used either alone or in connection with other mouldings.

Arc.—In geometry, a portion of the circumference of a circle or other curve line.

Arcade.—A covered passage composed generally of a range of arches, supported either on columns or piers, and detached from or attached to the wall.

Arch.—A concave or hollow structure supported by its own curve.

A number of wedge-shaped stones disposed in the line of some curve, and supporting each other by their mutual pressure.

The arch itself is composed of voussoirs, or arch stones, the uppermost of which is called the key-stone.—*See* Plates IV. & V.

Architrave.—The lower of the three principal members of the entablature of an order, being the chief beam resting immediately on the columns.

A collection of mouldings round a door, window, or other aperture.—*See also* **Entablature.**

Archivolt.—The band of mouldings round the arch stones of an arch, which terminates horizontally upon the impost.

Arris.—The line or edge on which two surfaces forming an exterior angle meet each other, either plane or curved.

Ashlar.—A term for hewn or squared stone, as distinguished from unwrought material ; it is generally used for facings, and set in horizontal courses, and bears various names according to the manner in which it is worked, such as Plain Ashlar, Tooled Ashlar, Rustic Ashlar, &c.—*See* Plate X.

Astragal.—A small moulding of a semicircular profile. The name is generally applied to the necking separating the capital from the column—*See also* **Moulding.**

Axis of a Cylinder.—A right line passing through the solid, from the centre of one of the circular ends to the centre of the other, and the line on which such a body may be conceived to revolve.

Axis of a Dome.—A right line perpendicular to the horizon, passing through the centre of its base.—*See* Plate XXXII.

Banker.—A block of stone forming a bench on which the stone is worked.

Base.—In geometry, the lower part of a figure or body.

The base of a solid is the surface on which it rests.

In masonry, the lower moulded part, between the shaft and the pedestal.

Batter.—A wall that inclines inward from a vertical or plumb line, so that the upper part of the surface falls within the base.

Bed.—The horizontal surface on which a stone lies. The beds of a stone are the surfaces where the stones meet ; the upper surface is called the top bed, and the under surface the bottom bed.—*See also* **Natural Bed.**

Billet Moulding.—A Norman moulding used in arches, strings, &c. ; it consists of small short lengths of beads or bars, cut in hollow mouldings, with spaces between equal to the length of the billet.—*See* Plate XLVII., Figs. 31 & 32. *See also* **Moulding.**

Blocking-course.—A course of stones placed on the top of a cornice, forming the summit of the wall.

Boasting.—Cutting the stone roughly to form of intended carving.

Bond.—The disposition or lapping of the stones so that vertical joints may not fall over one another, but fall directly over the middle of the stone below, in order to form an inseparable mass of building.

Bond-stone.—Stones whose longest horizontal direction is placed in the thickness of the work, for the purpose of binding the wall together.

Boning.—The art of testing a plane surface by the guidance of the eye and the aid of two straight-edges, by which it is seen whether the work is out of winding, or whether the surface be plane or twisted.—*See* Plate IX., Figs. 1 & 2.

Boss.—A sculptured or carved projection to conceal the intersection of the moulded ribs in a vault, or at the stop end of a string course or label.—*See* Plate XLI.

Breaking Joint.—The placing of a stone over the course below, in such a position that the joint above shall not fall vertically directly over the joint below it.

Buttress.—A pier of masonry projecting from a wall to support and strengthen it. Buttresses are employed in Gothic buildings to resist the thrust of the vaulting and roof, and also to stiffen walls and towers of great height.

Camber.—The slightly hollowed soffit given to a lintel or flat arch to correct the apparent sinking down in the centre.

Canopy.—An ornamental projection over windows, doors, niches, &c.

Cant.—An external splay angle cut off a square.

Cantilever.—A large projecting bracket to support cornices, balconies, eaves, &c.

Capital.—The head or uppermost member of a column, pier, or pilaster, in any part of a building, but generally applied to that of a column or pilaster of the several orders.—*See* CAPS, Plates XLVII. to LII.

Chamfer.—The arris of a solid cut to a bevelled plane.

Chevron.—A zigzag or V-shaped ornament used in mouldings, chiefly to arches in Norman work.—*See* Plate XLVII., Fig. 35.

Chiselled Work.—The surface of a stone formed by the chisel.

Chord.—In geometry, a straight line drawn from any point of an arc to any other point of that arc.

Circle.—A plane figure, of which its boundary is everywhere at an equal distance from a point within its surface, called its centre.

Its perimeter encloses the largest area of any figure.

Circular Work.—A term applied to any work with cylindric or spherical faces.

Circumference.—The curve line which bounds the area of a circle.

Circumscribe.—To draw a line round a figure so as to enclose it.

Closer.—The last stone fixed in a horizontal course which is usually of less dimensions than the others.

Coffer.—A sunk panel in vaults, domes, and arches. The name is also applied to any sunk panel in a ceiling or soffit.

Column.—A cylindrical or polygonal pier, which supports a superincumbent weight in a vertical direction ; it is generally composed of a base, shaft, and capital.—*See also* **Pilaster.**

Concave.—A hollow line or surface, as the soffit of an arch, vault, or the inner surface of a sphere.

Concentric.—Having the same centre but different radii.

Conic Sections.—The figures formed by the intersections of a plane with a cone, which do not include the triangle or the circle. These three sections are the ellipse, parabola, and hyperbola.

Contour.—The outline of a figure or body ; the line that bounds.

Convex.—A rising or swelling on the exterior surface into a round or spherical form, as the outside of a sphere, the extrados of an arch, &c.

Coping.—The highest and top covering course in a wall.

Corbel.—A small bracket projecting from the wall to support some superincumbent weight.

Cornice.—A horizontal projection, moulded, decorated, or otherwise, which crowns or terminates a wall, building, pedestal, or other piece of work.—*See* Plate IX., Fig. 4.

Course.—A row of stones of the same height generally placed on a level bed. The stones round the face and intrados of an arch, are also called a course of stones.

Coursing Joint.—The joint between two courses of stone.

Crown of an Arch.—The highest or central part of an arch or any arched surface.—*See* Plates IV. & V.

Cupola.—A concave ceiling or roof, hemispherical or nearly so. A small dome.

Curtail Step.—The first or bottom step of a stairs, generally of a curved form on plan, and a curved quoin end.   P

Curve Line.—A concave or convex line.

Cusp.—A triangular projection from an inner curve of a tracery arch or window. —*See* Plate XLVI., Fig. 10.

Cylinder.—A circular body of uniform diameter, whose ends or base form equal parallel circles, and whose curved surface is everywhere at an equal distance from its axis.

The cone, sphere, and cylinder have a relative value to each other, namely, that the cone is one-third the cylinder having the same base and height ; and the inscribed sphere two-thirds of the cylinder, or the cone, sphere, and cylinder are to each other as the numbers 1, 2, 3.—*See* Plate IX., Fig. 3.

Cylindrical Work.—Any form of work which partakes of the shape of a cylinder.

Dentils.—The small square blocks or teeth cut in the bed mould of cornices, pediments, &c.—*See* Plate IX., Fig. 5.

Development.—The unrolling or laying out of a surface upon a plane, so that every point of the surface may coincide with the plane.

Diagonal.—A straight line drawn through a plane figure, joining two opposite angles.

Diameter.—A straight line passing through the centre of a curvilinear figure, and dividing the figure symmetrically into two equal parts, terminating in the circumference on each side, as that of a circle or ellipse.

Diminution of a Column.—The gradual contraction of the diameter of a column, so that the upper diameter is less than the lower.—*See* Plate XI., Figs. 7 & 8.

Dome.—The spherical or convex roof raised over a circular or polygonal building. There is great variety in the forms of domes, both in plan and section. *See* Plate XXXII.—*See also* **Cupola.**

Draft.—A margin on the surface of a stone, dressed to the width of the chisel or bolster, for the purpose of directing its reduction to the required surface.

Dressed.—A term which expresses the preparation a stone has undergone, before fixing in its position in the building.

Edge.—The meeting in an external angle of two planes or surfaces of a solid.

Elevation.—A geometrical projection drawn on a plane perpendicular to the horizon.

Ellipse or Ellipsis.—One of the conic sections, produced by cutting a cone by a plane passing obliquely through the opposite sides. It may be divided into two equal and similar parts, by a diameter drawn in any direction.

Entablature.—The superstructure which lies horizontally upon architectural columns. It consists of three portions ; the architrave, which rests immediately upon the columns, the frieze or central portion, and the cornice.

Entasis.—A refined and almost imperceptible swelling of the shaft of a column.—*See* Plate IX., Figs. 7 & 8.

Equiangular.—Having equal angles.

Equidistant.—At equal distances.

Equilateral.—Having equal sides.

Extrados.—The exterior or convex curve of an arch.—*See* Plate IV., Fig. 1.

Face-mould.—A pattern or templet defining the form to which a stone is to be worked. It is usually made of sheet zinc.

Fillet.—A small moulding of square section. Also the space between two flutings in a column or pilaster.

Finial.—The top or finishing terminal to a gable or pinnacle.

Flush.—The bedding of masonry blocks in mortar or cement, completely filling in all interstices in the beds and joints.

The term is also used to signify the breaking off or chipping any portion of a dressed stone.

Flute.—A perpendicular hollow or channel ; used to decorate the shafts of columns or pilasters.

Flyers.—Steps in a flight of stairs, whose edges are parallel to each other.—*See* Plate XII.

Foci.—The two points in the major axis of an ellipse to which a string may be fixed so as to describe the curve.

Free-stone.—A stone which can be freely worked in any direction.

Gargoyle.—A projecting waterspout usually carved into a grotesque head.

Gauge.—The measure to which any dimension is confined.

Geometry.—The science which explains, and the art which shews, the construction of lines, angles, plane figures, and solids.

Grit-stone.—A coarse or fine-grained sandstone of various degrees of hardness. It is composed of small grains of sand united by a cementing material of an argillaceous, calcareous, or siliceous nature.

Groin.—The curved line formed by the intersection of two arches or vaults crossing each other at any angle.—*See* Plate XXVII.

Groined Vault.—" One formed by three or more curved surfaces, so that every two may form a groin, all the groins terminating at one extremity in a common point."—" Gwilt."—*See* Plate XXXIV. and following.

Ground Line.—The straight line upon which the vertical plane of projection is placed.

Grout.—A thin semi-liquid mortar composed of cement and sand or lime and sand, and run into the joints and beds of stonework, filling all interstices.

Gypsum.—" Crystals of native sulphate of lime. Being subjected to a moderate heat, to expel the water of crystallisation, it forms plaster of Paris, and, coming in contact with water, immediately assumes a solid form. Of the numerous species, alabaster is, perhaps, the most abundant."—" Gwilt."

Header.—Stones extending through the thickness of a wall, as bond-stones.

Heading.—The vertical side of a stone perpendicular to the face.

Heading Joint.—The thin stratum of mortar between the vertical surfaces of two adjacent stones.

Helix.—A spiral winding round the surface of a cylinder.— *See* Plate XIV.

Hemisphere.—One half of a globe or sphere, when divided through its centre by a plane.

Hypothenuse.—The longest side of a right-angled triangle. The side opposite to the right angle.

Impost.—The capital of a pier or pilaster from which an arch springs Its form varies in the different orders.

Inclination.—The angle contained between a line and a plane, or between two planes.

Intersection.—The point on which two lines meet and cut each other. The line in which two surfaces cut or meet each other.

Intrados.—The inner curve of an arch.—*See* Plate IV., Fig. 1.

Jambs.—The vertical sides of a window or door opening, which connect the two sides of a wall.

Joggle.—An indentation made in one stone, called the she joggle, to receive the projection on another termed the he joggle. *See* Plate VII.

Joint.—The surface of contact between two adjacent blocks of stone.

Jumper.—A long steel chisel used for drilling holes.—*See* Plate I., Fig. 18.

Key Course.—The horizontal range of stones in the summit of a vault, in which the course is placed.

Key Stone.—The highest central stone in the crown of an arch.—*See* Plate IV., Fig. 1. *See* **Arch.**

Label.—The drip or hood moulding over the apertures in Gothic windows and doors.

Lancet Arch.—Narrow window heads shaped like the point of a lancet, and characteristic of the Early English Gothic (13th century).

Landing.—The terminating floor of a flight of stairs, either above or below it ; or the level part of a staircase connecting one flight with another. *See* Plate XII., Fig. 2.

Level.—A line or surface horizontal or parallel to the horizon ; or a straight line perpendicular to a plumb line.

Line of Batter.—The line of section made by a plane and the surface of a battering wall, the plane being perpendicular both to the surface of the wall and to the horizon.

Lintel.—A stone which extends over the aperture of a door or window, and carries the superincumbent weight by means of its strength or resistance.

Marble.—"A term limited by mineralogists and geologists to the several varieties of carbonate of lime, having more or less of a granular and crystalline texture. It is susceptible of a very fine polish, and the varieties of it are extremely numerous."—" Gwilt."

Marble, Polishing of.—Marbles are of such a varied nature that one method of polishing cannot be adopted for all, although the following method will suffice for Statuary, Vein, Sicilian, St. Anne's, and most of the ordinary coloured marbles in general use.

The wrought surface is rubbed with fine sharp sand and water, until all the marks of the chisel or saw are removed, and an even face is produced; it is then "grounded," that is, rubbed with grit stones of varying degrees of fineness, commencing with the coarse or "first grit," next the "second grit," which is a little finer, and then finishing with "snake" or "Water of Ayr" stone. Particular care must be taken that in each process of "gritting" the marks or scratches of its predecessor are removed, so that when the surface is "snaked" no scratches whatever are visible, but left quite smooth, for upon the careful "gritting" depends the success of the ultimate polish.

The polishing is lastly effected by rubbing with a pad of felt sprinkled with putty powder (calcined tin) moistened with water, until the gloss or natural polish is obtained.

The polishing of marble adds greatly to its beauty, inasmuch as its delicate figuring, and gradations of rich colouring, are brought out and heightened by the process, which thus makes it so valuable as a decorative material.

Masonry.—The art of shaping, arranging, and uniting stones, in the construction of walls and other parts of buildings.

Metopes.—The square spaces between triglyphs in the frieze of the Doric order; sometimes applied to the sculptures fitted into these spaces.

Modillion.—A projecting enriched bracket in the soffit of the top bed of a cornice.

Monolith.—Consisting of one stone.

Mortise.—A sinking in a stone to receive a corresponding projection.

Mould.—A templet or pattern defining the form of the stone which is to be worked. It is usually made of sheet zinc.

Moulding.—The outline or contour given to an angle whether a projection or a cavity.

Mouldings may be generally resolved into three elementary forms—hollow, round, and square—and it is upon the choice, arrangement, and proportion of these forms that beauty or ugliness depends. Of the two main principles in connection with mouldings, namely, projection and recession, the former is generally adopted in Classical and Renaissance architecture, and the latter in Gothic. The most perfect profiles are such as are composed of few mouldings, varied and alternating both in form and size, fitly applied with regard to their uses, and so disposed that the straight and curved members succeed each other alternately. In every profile there should be a prominent member, to which all the others should be subservient, and appear to support and fortify, or to shelter it from injury by the weather.

The best known examples are as follows:—

Fillet, Listel or Square .   Astragal or Bead .

Ovolo or Quarter Round   Torus or Tore

Ogee or Cyma Reversa .   Cyma Recta or Cymatium

Cavetto or Hollow .   Scotia . . .

The above refer to mouldings of the Roman Orders.—*See also* Plates XLVII. to LII.

Mullion.—The upright post or bars of stone which subdivide a window into two or more lights. *See also* **Transom.**

Mural.—Belonging or attached to a wall.

Mutule.—A projecting ornament in a Doric cornice, somewhat resembling the end of a timber beam; it occupies the place of the modillion in the other orders.

Natural Bed of a Stone.—The direction in which the natural strata lie when in the quarry.

The line of the planes of cleavage.

Newel.—The vertical column or pillar about which, in a winding stair, the steps turn, and receive support from the bottom to the top.

The newel step in an open stair is the bottom one; it is generally curvilinear on plan.—*See* Plates XII. & XIV.

Niche.—A semicircular or hollow recess generally within the thickness of a wall, for a statue, vase, or other ornament.—*See* Plates XXV. & XXVI.

Normal.—A right line perpendicular to the tangent of a curve.

Ordinate.—"A line drawn from any part of the circumference of an ellipse or other conic section, perpendicular to, and across the axis to the other side." —"Gwilt."

Parabola.—One of the three conic sections.

An open curve of which both of its branches may be extended infinitely without ever meeting.

It is produced by cutting a cone by a plane parallel to one of its sides, and so named because its axis is parallel to the side of the cone.

Parallel.—Lines, surfaces, &c., that are in every part equidistant from each other, and extended in the same direction.

Pediment.—A triangular, or gabled termination to a building, sometimes also placed over doors, windows, porticoes, &c.

Perpendicular.—A line at right angles to a given line.

Pier, Pillar.—*See* **Column.**

Pilaster.—A square column usually attached to a wall from which it projects.

In most cases it corresponds to the columns of its order, having a similar capital, shaft, and base.

Plane.—A perfectly flat or level surface, coinciding in every direction with a straight line.

Plinth.—The base of a wall, column, &c.

Profile.—The contour outline of mouldings taken at right angles to their length.

Projection.—The art of representing any object on a plane by means of straight lines, drawn from all visible parts of those objects to intersect the plane of projection.

Quadrant.—The fourth part of a circle ; an arc of ninety degrees.

Quoins.—The courses of stone to any external angle of a building.

Radiating Joints.—Those joints which tend to a centre.—*See* Plates IV. & V.

Radius.—A right line drawn from the centre to the circumference of a circle. The semidiameter of a circle or sphere.

Raking Mouldings.—Mouldings which run in an inclined position.—*See* Plate X., Figs. 11 & 12.

Rib.—A narrow arch-formed bar projecting beyond the surface of a vault, to mark its intersection and to add strength.—*See* Plate XXXVI., Fig. 10.

Rustic Quoins.—The coursed stones to the external angles of a building, projecting beyond the face of the wall.

Sandstone.—A stone composed of grains of sand, united with other mineral substances, cemented together by a material of an argillaceous, calcareous, or siliceous nature.

Scribe.—To scratch in on the stone, with a sharp pointed tool, the profile of a mould, templet, &c.

Section.—The figure formed by cutting a solid by a plane.

Segment of a Circle.—A portion of a circle contained by an arc and its chord.

Setting.—A term used to denote the fixing of dressed stones in their proper position in the walls of buildings.

Shaft.—The cylindrical part of a column between the base and the capital. *See* Plate XI., Figs. 7 & 8.

Soffit or Sofite.—The under surface of any part of a ceiling, architrave, arch, vault, stairs, &c.

Soffit Joints.—Those joints which appear on the under surface.

Span.—The distance or dimension across the opening of an arch, window, or aperture. *See* Plate IV., Fig. 1.

Spandrel.—A triangular-shaped piece. The irregular triangular space between the curve of an arch and the rectangle inclosing it ; or the space between the outer mouldings of two contiguous arches and a horizontal line above them.

Spiral. —The helix or screw. A curve consisting of one or more revolutions round a fixed point and gradually receding from it.

Spire.—A steeple diminishing as it ascends, generally octagonal on plan.

Splay.—A slope making with the face of a wall an angle less than a right angle.

Stair.—One step of a series by means of which a person ascends or descends to a different landing.

A series of steps for passing from one part of a building to another. *See* Plates XII., XIII., XIV. & XV.

Staircase.—A flight of stairs with their supporting framework, casing, balusters, &c., which enable persons to ascend or descend from one floor to another. *See* Plate XII., Fig. 2.

Stilted Arch.—An arch in which the springing line or curve does not commence for some distance above the level of the impost.

Stone Cutting.—The art of hewing or dressing stones to their intended form.

Straight-Edge.—A rule whose edge coincides with a straight line.

Stretcher.—A stone laid with its longer face in the surface of the wall.

Tangent.—A straight line which touches a curve without cutting it.

Tangent Plane.—A plane which touches a curved surface without being able to cut it.

Templet.—A mould giving the contour to which stones are to be wrought.

Transom.—A horizontal bar across a window of two or more lights. *See also* **Mullion.**

Triangle.—A plane figure consisting of three sides.

Trihedral.—A solid angle consisting of three plane angles.

Trisection.—The division into three equal parts.

Tympanum.—The triangular face of a pediment included between the horizontal and raking mouldings.

Vault.—An arched roof or ceiling over an apartment, so constructed that the stones of which it is composed sustain and keep each other in their places. *See* Plates XXVII. to XXIX. & XXXIV. to XLI.

Vertical Plane.—A plane perpendicular to the horizon.

Volute.—A spiral scroll as in the Ionic capital.

Voussoir.—A wedge-shaped stone forming one of the blocks of an arch. *See* Plate IV., Fig. 1.

Weathering.—A sloping surface of stone employed to cover the set-off of a wall or buttress, and protect it from the effects of the weather.

Welch Groin.—A groin formed by the intersection of two cylindrical vaults, one being of greater height than the other.

Winder.—One in a flight of steps which are curved on plan, having each tread broader at one end than the other. *See* Plates XIII. & XIV.

Wreathed Column.—Twisted in the form of a screw or spiral.

MASONRY CONSERVATION AND RESTORATION

A S Ireson

The issue of a new book dealing with the art and craft of stone masonry is a very rare event. The author is well known as a writer, sculptor, stonemasonry consultant and conservationist. He was a co-founder of The Men of the Stones and of The Orton Trust and holds the Lord Esher Award for his work on the restoration of historic buildings. He was co-author with Alec Clifton-Taylor of *English Stone Building* published by Gollancz and has written numerous short works on local history and architecture.

Masonry Conservation and Restoration is the culmination of a lifetimes' involvement in the stone industry and incorporates much oral tradition as well as personal experience in carrying out contracts for the conservation and restoration of stone buildings of all ages and styles. The contents includes:

Survey of work to be carried out – specifications and quantities – estimates – contracts and cost control – selection of stone – preparation of stone – mortars, sand and pointing – special scaffolds – cleaning, consolidation and toning – surface treatments etc.

The book includes a foreword by Sir Bernard Fielden CBE., FSA., RIBA and incorporates a bibliography, glossary of terms and a list of specialist material suppliers.

A4 paperback fully illustrated about 56 pages.
ISBN 0 948083 19 0 2nd Ed

ATTIC

BOOKS